C000016627

FARM FATALE

Farm Fatale

PAUL HEINEY

Excellent Press
Ludlow

First published in 2012 by Excellent Press
9 Lower Raven Lane
Ludlow SY8 1BL

Text © 2012 by Paul Heiney

Reprinted December 2012

British Library in Cataloguing Publishing Data:
A catalogue entry for this publication is available
from the British Library

ISBN 978 1 900318 44 0

Printed in Great Britain

CONTENTS

INTRODUCTION

The contents of this book were written over a period of nearly thirty years and I have brought them together now because I believe that, taken as a whole, they tell a story far greater than I ever envisaged when I first wrote them. It is as if a heap of random jigsaw pieces have revealed an unexpected picture.

When I first set pen to paper, I was a young man newly enthralled by the world of top-rating television – I was one of the *That's Life* team – and by the time I came to write the final words in this book I had just emerged from an intensive, inspiring, yet often heartbreaking decade as an organic farmer who had, with single mind, turned back the clock to the days when the land was farmed with carthorses. It is an unusual career path. It is only recently that I have realised that what I recorded over nearly thirty years had, piece by piece, charted the course of this extraordinary transition.

Britain abounds with people who love the countryside and everything about it, but few have come to it by taking the route I chose; and even fewer have gained an understanding of the land and its people by immersing themselves as deeply into its culture as I have done.

I would never have put pen to paper in the first place if it had not been for the publishers of *In at the Deep End, Pulling Punches,* and several Editors of the *The Times* who ran my *Farmer's Diary* weekly for almost a decade. Because of them, I am able to present the whole story to you now.

Paul Heiney
Suffolk 2012

ONE

The moment I decided that I needed a farm of my own, and to work the soil with my own hands, was the moment the earth moved. It felt like an earthquake; it had the force of a life-changing tremor and to this day, twenty years later, I still feel the shock waves. I was just forty years old, with a comfortable little career; yet out of the blue I decided to become a farmer. This is the story of how I came to arrive at this great turning point in my life, and the tears, laughter, joy and despair that flowed from it.

At the precarious stage of mid life at which I had arrived, men often seek comfort from the lengthening shadow of the passing years by investing in new wives, or Jaguar cars. I opted instead for 40 acres of Suffolk and three large, brown carthorses. To this already heady mixture I added several sheds full of vintage farm machinery which bore the rust of decades and the scars of mechanical abuse. I like to think my farming career did not come to an end on a scrap heap, but it certainly started on one.

Imagine, then, a shallow little valley on the Suffolk coastal strip, a few miles inland from the sea. Along the bottom of the Vale runs a stream; no more than a damp ditch, really. On either side are large arable fields cultivated by monstrous pieces of machinery to grow and harvest the wheat, barley and rape for which this fertile part of England is famous. Standing alongside these fields, hiding behind trees as if in shame, you catch a glimpse of a relic of a farming age long past. There is a black barn, and an old stable where cart horses last stood fifty years before and where they now stand again. There are many roof tiles missing, and much of the brick and woodwork no longer has a close association with the vertical. And if you look closely, you will see a lone figure standing in the midst of all this, wondering what the hell he has done. For now this is my farm; my folly, perhaps. This is where the drama of the following decade will unfold.

On my new farm there is a tumbledown barn that leans precariously away from the wind and creaks at every gust. There are rusty iron gutters along the edge of gaping roofs. Inside the crumbling buildings, wooden mangers are rubbed smooth where greedy bovine tongues once licked every ounce of corn from them. And in the soft red brick are scratched the initials of the men who, a century ago, did what I am going to try to do today. I am going to be a farmer.

Not a modern farmer. I am not going in for the current state-of-the-art agriculture which demands maximum return at whatever expense to land, animal or planet. I want to have the sort of farm of which children's books were written, where chickens scratched at the foot of haystacks, pigs rooted in corners of fields (for whatever it is that pigs root so earnestly for) and where lambs frolicked in meadows.

Stinking tractors won't get a look-in either: I have bought three mighty carthorses, Suffolk Punches, which will reap and sow, plough and mow, carthorses doing what they were bred for. And there I shall be, at the centre of it all, leaning over the five-bar gate dispensing dubious rural wisdom to passers-by. Think of Old MacDonald and his farm, and you've got it.

But my farm will be no joke. I know that many modern farmers will already be laughing their socks off at the thought that a smug ex-townie with his old horse can teach them anything about growing food. All I would say is that within the walls of my crumbling farmyard buildings lies a fossilised wisdom which is about to have its resurrection.

4

The farming clock has to be turned back to the days when farming made sense. Few people these days seem to like farmers very much, which is unhealthy. They feed us cheaply and plentifully and we ought to be able to trust them. Fifty years ago, farmers were perceived as jolly chaps who ploughed the fields and scattered till all was safely gathered in. No one sings hymns of praise about farming these days. It's a dark subject.

I think I can throw some light on it. The men who scratched their initials in the soft brick of my tumbledown farm, 'A.J.P. 1867' or 'P. ELY 1892', were farming under a system which was better than any invented since, and from which we could still learn a lot. They worked in harmony with natural systems rather than trying to fight them. The muck their animals produced, to take one example, was not the embarrassment it is today. 'A.J.P.', whoever he was, would have laughed. He knew how to keep stock and feed his land for free. The simplicity was the beauty of the system. He grew the corn and saved the straw. When winter drew on, the stock were brought from the meadows into the farmyard for shelter and to be fed. Down their throats went some of his precious corn and, obligingly, the animal deposited the digested remains in neat little pats on the very straw that had carried the corn the summer long.

After six months of being trodden by ever heavier hooves in the farmyard, a miraculous transformation would have taken place; for when 'A.J.P.' stuck his fork into the muck he found it had turned into dark, rich, nutritious, rotted compost. It had cost him nothing at all. The horse and cart were sent for, and an army of men, and forkful by sticky forkful the precious matter was carted to the field to be ploughed in, to help grow more corn, to feed more stock, to produce more straw, to fill the yards in the winter. 'E-i-e-i-o,' as Old MacDonald would have said. And so revolved a highly efficient and natural cycle. It was organic farming before anyone had come up with the idea.

Will it work today, on my farm? To the satisfaction of my critics, who will be many, I have to admit that it may not. Not on the small scale I can afford to do it. It is not because the natural system was in any way at fault: it is just that the figures don't add up any more. Yields of corn on the old farms were much lower than today, labour was cheaper, there was plenty of it and farmers did not feel they had a right to a rich living. So, to prove that the old farming was the best farming for the land and the countryside, if not the modern pocket, I am personally putting on my boots and taking to the soil. It is the principle that matters, and the pounds will have to take care of themselves. It will cost all my family's spare income at first and cause some anxiety. But I don't care.

The farm runs to only forty acres. Not big, hardly room enough for an out-of-town Tesco, but it will do to prove the point. Thankfully it has been in good hands, for the fields still have their hedges, the trees are standing and the first-class barn has not been converted into a second-class house.

By East Anglian standards, the countryside is hilly. From the highest point of the farm I can stand and smell, if not quite see, the sea. From the highest point, I hope, in a few years' time, to look down on a farm as it would have looked a hundred years ago: fields of corn grown organically without the help of synthetic fertilisers and pesticides, pastures rich in herbs and grasses that give the animals that graze them a glow of good health. Horses will be at work, too. In winter, Suffolk Punches might be carting hay or turnips to sheep. If it is June they will pull the mower that cuts the grass to make hay. We shall cart the hay to the farmyard and with our pitchforks build haystacks. Remember those? In the winter the horses will labour before the plough turning the used earth and making it new again.

In the meantime, I have considerable gaps in my knowledge to fill. Modern farming textbooks were clearly of no use so my education was gleaned from such diverse volumes as *Stephen's Book of the Farm: Second Edition, 1877* and *Mayhew's Illustrated Horse Management, 1890*. I gather from the style supplements of the Sunday newspapers that we are judged by the books that we are seen to be reading in public; Martin Amis and Julian Barnes are pretty high on the list of desirables. Alas, there was no mention of *Humus and the Farmer – A Critical View* or *The Pioneering Pig*, two volumes from which I have recently found great inspiration.

I fell in the style index. Baffled media people began to get scripts returned with wisps of straw between the pages and with pig carcass prices scribbled up the margin. The envelopes smelt horribly because the foolish boy who brought the pig-feed put it down on the pile of letters. If, by the way, there is a publisher who finds a set of rubber rings for castrating sheep mixed in with a manuscript, they're quite expensive and I'd like them back.

But slowly I am learning about farming. And about farmers. I went to see one of the old timers the other day to try to buy off him a horse-drawn plough. He took me into the yard where it stood, and told me the full story.

'It was my father's,' he pined. 'Good old plough it is, he taught me everything he knew behind that old plough. No, that's an old family friend really. I couldn't sell that ...' and he took a long pause, and with a knowing look said, '... unless that was for a hundred pounds!' Sly old devil.

I shall need a touch of cunning like that if the money is not to run out entirely. I don't suppose I'll get much support from serious farmers. They will dismiss it all as fanciful romanticism, unaware that the sands of time are running out for the system they uphold. My extreme reaction is probably not the answer either, but it is a gesture.

If I have anyone on my side, I hope it will be the spirits of 'A.J.P.' and 'P. ELY' for they, and men like them, created a science of farming that deserves better than to be dismissed as inefficient and sentimental rubbish. I am about to start on what for me will be a great adventure. As I put the collars on the horses and we take to the fields to work, I shall think of those men. I hope they will be with me on every long trudge down the furrow.

As any countryman worthy of the name will tell you, before any flower blooms there must be green shoots as it first springs into life. So what of my green shoots, this unexpected bursting forth of agricultural longings that eventually blossomed into a love and affection or all things to do with the land? Where were they to be found. To be honest, they're hard to spot for they lay as well hidden as a sixpence at the bottom of a mean farmer's pocket. There was nothing obvious in my life that you could point to and say 'that was where it all started'. So, we must first examine the soil in which these unexpected shoots grew to see what kind of seed might have been sown.

TWO

Sheffield, in the early fifties, would appear to be the least green place imaginable. It was still a proud City of Steel where furnaces belched fire into the night air, where the heavy impact of huge hammers forged ingots into sheets and rods of the best steel that Britain could make. Hundreds of tall chimneys lined the Don Valley, each spewing thick smoke more suffocating than vitalising; a reassurance, though, that industry was alive and kicking and there'd be money in the wage packet at the end of the week. The prosperity that steel-making brought came at a heavy cost for the air was often so thick you could taste it, the poor old Town Hall was black from the pollution, the upper decks of the buses packed with coughing and spitting steel workers who misguidedly thought that their already damaged lungs would be further preserved by a steady intake of Capstan Full Strength. It made for a difficult choice for an eleven year old who had to travel the entire width of the city to get to his grammar school, for the upper deck of the bus was the only place to be and be seen by your classmates. To travel on the lower, smokeless, deck was to be mocked. But the top decks were filthy places, filled with Park Drive smog and the slimy residues left by those who ignore the 'No Spitting' signs – some of those upper decks you could skate on. The daily slog between home to school was no pastoral jaunt from Lark Rise to Candleford.

If I wanted to divorce myself even further from rurality, I could always visit my father at work. He drove the lorry that dumped the ash that poured out of the coal fired power station at Neepsend. He worked from a concrete hut, eight feet square, with a tin roof and not much bigger than an air-raid shelter, which had a bunk bed and a billy stove on which he burned fearsome power station coal which gave out a near nuclear heat. From here he could watch the vast hoppers which filled at varying speeds according to the electrical demands of the people of Sheffield, and he would empty them as required by driving his lorry beneath the hopper, filling it, and then driving the load of hot ash to the top of waste mountain that he himself was building, load by load. There's a housing estate on it now.

So that was his working life lived in the shadow of an ever-growing mountain of waste which, load by load, he was turning into a cliff face of shifting black ash which towered over that little hut. When he died, not yet fifty, we buried him in a cemetery high on a Sheffield hill. That was probably the safest he'd been in his life. This was a man who bravely fought with the Poles at Monte Cassino, was forced into a shotgun marriage with my mother, and drank so heavily that we felt sure that one night he would reverse his lorry too far and come tumbling down that ash heap. In the end, his heart gave out. I understand now that it had been broken long before, when the invading Nazis forced him and his family out of their native Poland, capturing his brothers whom he never saw again.

If Sheffield had a redeeming feature, it was that like Rome it was built on hills. And between them flowed the River Don and its various tributaries which provided the water that first made the place into somewhere that steel could be manufactured. All Sheffield kids learnt this in geography lessons. For me, though, the hills felt not confining but offered instead a promise of release. You never had to walk far before you were offered a tantalizing glimpse of somewhere greener or a place the sun might always shine through a clear rather than a smoky sky. The horizon, whether on land or at sea, has always drawn me to it, and I am sure it was those views which gave me a taste for it. From the kitchen where we sat for glum family meals (I was an only child), the window gave a broad view for miles across to the west, from where the weather came. As I sat at that table, I often wondered what it would be like on the far side of those hills. What lay beyond?

Sheffield's greatest virtue, it always seemed to me, was that it was entirely surrounded by lovely places to go – there was always escape. To the north were the Pennines, to the south the Derbyshire Dales. To the east are the flat flood plains of the River Don on which the steelworks were built, but even these soon give way to farmland and eventually the coast, four hours away into our old Hillman Minx. We had a weekend pastime called 'going out for a run'. It meant getting in the car, feeling instantly sick, and heading off to distant Derbyshire or delightful Bakewell and Chatsworth House, or north to the foothills of the Pennines, heading for open country where the air was fresh once you were through the village of Chapeltown where stood the pungent Izal Medicated Toilet Paper factory.

When there wasn't money for petrol, which was often the case, from home I could walk to the countryside in five minutes. It was a journey improved no end by a call on Mrs Molinari, an Italian immigrant with a fleet of two ice cream vans who had created an ice lolly made of Tizer. Then it was a brisk, uphill excursion, first past a farm where milk was offered over the gate but few people took up the offer because the place stank like hell, then down a winding lane which gave breathtaking views over the entire city before it forked with one road taking you downhill to the Bachelors Tinned Peas factory (which also stank, of rotting pea pods. It was where my mother had worked and ever after blamed the wet working conditions for her abiding swollen ankles). The other fork in the lane took you to another small cow farm which delivered milk to our street thanks to an old farmer who walked with an impossible limp but whose milk was reckoned to be the very best. We never bought from him, naturally, my mother preferring the watery Co-op offering.

I remember how much it meant to escape to the countryside, to turn your back on the dreariness of suburban housing clutter and see only fields, pathways and stone walls. This was somewhere to slide down hills on cardboard boxes, splash in streams, clamber over walls, have high adventures in the bushes, and generally let your young mind roam free. It was known to everyone as Back Edge, and it was a perfect name for the place for this was the back edge of the hellish city where it gave way to a greener land beyond. It was my release.

But is this the soil in which the green shoots of my farming life might be found? I doubt it. All the kids I knew were taking the same walks as I was, and playing the same games amongst the hills and fields, and none of them, as far as I know, ended up behind a pair of carthorses and loving everything about a farming life. So we must ask ourselves if it is 'in the blood'?

I once had this romantic idea that it might have come from my father's side, from his native Poland, which until recent years was a largely peasant economy where to own a pig and a patch of land was an insurance policy against everything life could throw at you which, in the case of the Poles, has been more misfortune than most of Europe put together. This, I assumed, was the green shoot I was looking for, genetically planted long before I was born and now pushing its way upwards through the topsoil of my life. I felt rather proud to be a descendant of earthy, peasant stock, till I discovered that my father's family came from a small town on the northern Polish plains which someone described to me as 'a bit like Barnsley' and certainly no more rural than the steel-making quarters of Sheffield. No joy there.

So did it come from the other side of the family? I remember my mother once watching me plough with horses. 'Yes,' she said, wistfully. 'I used to watch my father go up and down a field with horses just like you're doing.' I did not immediately seize on this for it had always been my understanding that my maternal grandfather died of throat cancer, having spent most of his working life in the smoke and fumes of Moss and Gamble's steel works in Wadsley Bridge which boasted the largest steam hammer in Sheffield which could be heard for miles around. Before the age of sixty he had inhaled enough steely smog to destroy his lungs, and I had never heard anyone remark that he had ever done anything else in his working life, certainly nothing to do with the land. My mother was also prone to romantic ramblings which gave me even less confidence in this family memory. Words would often spill from her mouth like confetti at the marriage of real and imagined events in her mind. Every time we passed the old Sheffield Royal Infirmary she would say, darkly, 'they took your Uncle Bert in there. Froze him and took his brain out.' She was prone to melodrama and had a ghoulish fear of hospitals believing 'they have the smell of death'. So I always regarded the fanciful story of Uncle Bert's brain as another of her ramblings. It was only many years later that I discovered he had been the subject of pioneering surgery, and although it may not have happened as crudely as she described, she may have not been a million miles from the truth. Accordingly, I must not dismiss that fact that my maternal grandfather may have been ploughing glorious furrows in his younger days, and I may be a fine example of how all our futures are somehow written in our past.

THREE

I don't know what a countryman would think of the world of broadcasting in which I have spent nearly all of my working life. What's to show for it, he might ask. Nothing. As soon as it is created it is gone. It is not entirely unlike the farming life, though; for the farmer nurtures his crop of wheat only to destroy it when it looks at its finest. The farming life also has its ups and downs, swings and roundabouts, feasts and famines and both are conducted under the guidance of an unseen hand; in the case of farming it is Mother Nature, in broadcasting no one is quite certain who is in charge but you can be pretty confident that they are not on your side. Over-confidence is a bad approach to both jobs; a farmer who is certain that he will produce a bumper crop is likely to be made a fool, and one who predicts that next week will be fine for harvest is sure to be put in his place. Likewise, anyone embarking on a career on the television would be wise to keep their ambitious thoughts to themselves for whoever is in charge will enjoy pouring a shower of cold rain on them just as much as God does when the farmer decides it is time to make hay. If you think farmers have a glum

13

view of life, you should spend a little time in studio dressing rooms.

There are other similarities between tillage and television. For a start, a working life on the telly is not entirely unlike a dispiriting trudge round the muddy headland of a field on a soggy day: both start briskly but soon slow as the weight of the heavy clay starts to sap the strength. There comes a point when you wonder if the field is worth walking round in the first place as the steps become heavier, the paces shorter, the rain torrential. Of course, there are crisp, sunny days and periods of great creativity when you kick the clay-like difficulties aside with a conviction that you will stride out towards the end of the earth and nothing will stop you. But, as in farming so it is in broadcasting, and soon the sky darkens, the first rain falls, and your sprint reverts to a more familiar trudge, one heavy footfall after another while you wonder if you might ever get to the end of the job in hand. This is not to say that I haven't enjoyed my working life, for I truly have. It has taken me to far more places in the world, and into the company of people beyond my imagining, than if I had accepted the fatal offer to most grammar school boys in Sheffield to 'come into the steel industry, lad. There'll always be a job'. Not five years after I left school, the steel mills started to close to be replaced by one of the largest shopping complexes in Europe. That must have thrown quite a few promised careers into the melting pot.

I had great years of fun and fame as part of the *That's Life* team, one of the BBC's highest ever rating shows, but after three series I sensed it was enough. But what next? The answer proved to be an unexpected television series for the BBC called *In at the Deep End*. It was an early form of reality television which was to feature me and Chris Serle, my companion on the back row of *That's Life*. We were to be engaged in various professions as novices, given training by people at the very top of those professions, and had to attain a measurable standard judged by way of a contest at the climax of the programme. Over the course of fifty minutes, the audiences would share the triumphs and humiliations of our punishing education as we tried to achieve in months what professionals had attained in lifetimes. The tasks were varied, demanding, and often humiliating. I was asked to perform as a stand-up comedian in drag – think of that gurning, northern character made immortal by the late Les Dawson – and was so embarrassingly, hair curlingly bad that the late Bernard Manning, having watched my act which was performed complete with an iron and a pile of washing, remarked, 'You'd have got more laughs auctioning the ironing board.' He was, of course, dead right. But those who saw success at these tasks as the only worthwhile outcome were missing the point, for there was far more to be learnt about the techniques and perils of stand-up comedy by watching my failure than there was by seeing someone breeze through it to thunderous applause. And the same applied to my efforts to write a romantic short story for *Woman's Weekly* – hugely demanding with a risible result from me – or the restyling of Jilly Cooper's hair under the tutorage of Vidal Sassoon – a poor result, I'm afraid, for Ms Cooper.

When the tasks were first presented to me I saw them as jobs to be done, stories to be told, a programme to be made, and although they would all require a considerable commitment it was a professional rather than a personal one. Like the lad who goes to a party seeking only a one-night-stand, I was not expecting to make any kind of deep commitment to any of the professions I was asked to master.

And then I fell in love. It was with a pair of gleaming white horses, Hungarian Greys, owned and driven by the master horseman John Parker who had a reputation as one of the country's top drivers of coaches and carriages. He was to be my tutor and teach me the skills needed to compete at a high level in the fiercely competitive world of carriage driving, which was in the public eye at the time due to the Duke of Edinburgh's very public participation. This felt a different kind of task, the only one which I welcomed with open arms. I knew from the moment it was mentioned that this would be something in which I would enjoy complete immersion. Of course, I knew not one end of a horse from the other and my only riding experience was on a weary old seaside donkey at Bridlington circa 1955. I knew neither horses nor horse people, but something clicked long before I had so much as picked up the reins.

On my first meeting with John Parker at his stables in the heart of East Anglia, there was no reason to believe that any bond might form between us. On the contrary, there was much suspicion on all sides. John was naturally cautious of anyone who sought to take up the sacred reins that only he liked to hold; and my reservations about 'horsey folk' were legion.

My first visit was in early September. A few battered carriages littered the stable yard, victims of a season's hard campaigning. John had a tired look too, but not from weariness; it is the way he always looks when there is doubt in his mind. On this occasion, his doubts were about me.

'I'm like a horse,' John said, forcefully. 'I don't like pigs and I don't like wind and neither do my horses.'

Behind him, a dozen white horses' heads appeared over the half-doors of their stables, steamy breath just visible in the chilly air. They sensed their master's curiosity and were making their own minds up about me.

'Have you ever driven a horse?' John asked, drawing on his miniature cigar.

'No, never,' I replied.

'Have you ever ridden one?' he asked, concerned now.

'No, never,' I replied, lamely.

'That's no hardship, I suppose,' he said after some consideration, 'but you've got to get one thing in your head. These horses …' They were all looking my way now, obediently emphasising their master's point, '… have got brains. They think as well as you do and that's why you've got to work as a team with the horses.'

'Do they know I'm a beginner?' I asked.

'They know exactly how much you know before you even touch the reins. You've got to gain their confidence in you. There's no point thinking it's easy because it ain't. It's 'ard.' And he gave me an equally long, 'ard look from under the brim of his brown horseman's trilby.

Introductions over, John took me for a drive. I sat on his left on what is known as the box seat, the raised platform on which the driver perches, and I watched his hands carefully. No great tugging or pulling, no sudden jerks like the stage coach drivers of Wells Fargo, no shouting of 'Yah!' or cracking of whips; just a subtle twist of wrist and finger with an occasional tensing of the arm – like playing a harp.

'It's more like fishing,' he said. 'You get a feeling. I know exactly when to pull. I can turn these horses by just twisting my hand.'

And he did. There and then. No fuss, no pulling. Just a flick of his wrist almost too subtle to see and they spun round and were heading the other way. Complete control.

We arrived at the village green and in the shadow of the moated castle (it was the deep water rather than the castle that first caught my attention; there's nothing like driving a carriage to make you ditch conscious) John handed me the reins and moved over to put me in the driving seat. One of the young girl grooms got down to hold the horses, like a driving instructor might put a wedge under the wheels while he nervously showed you the hill start. The reins travel all the way from your hand to the bit in the horse's mouth. That makes about twelve feet of leather down each side – no small weight. Halfway along, the rein splits into two and each part goes to the left hand side of each horse's mouth. The other rein also splits into two and each piece goes to the right hand side of the mouth. That way, two reins can control two horses.

'Don't let go or you're in dead trouble!' John warned.

I tried 'gee-up' as a starting signal. I might as well have said 'do you mind?' for all the effect it had.

'You don't listen,' said John. 'We don't say 'gee-up' we say 'walk on.''

I tried it. It worked. It was not the most tidy departure that two horses had ever made but at least we were mobile.

'Keep talking to them … Keep talking,' I could hear John say.

But what do you say to two horses whose names you don't even know? So I told them to walk on again. But they were walking already. I told them to whoooah! But they just lumbered on. So I urged them to walk on again. But what was the point; they were doing exactly as they wished? I got annoyed. After all, I wasn't doing anything that John Parker hadn't done when he was driving – I was holding the reins in the same way. But they did what he told them and ignored me. I couldn't see why, and felt a fool.

We lumbered round in circles for a good fifteen minutes when we should really have been going in straight lines. John's grooms were never far away in case I dropped the reins in exasperation, or through fatigue, and allowed the horses bolted for home. Then I caught sight of John, lighting up another cigar and grinning broadly.

'You were set up, boy!' he called and jumped back onto the box seat, taking the reins from me. 'I gave you the most difficult pair of horses I've got. You've got to be in this job for months before you can drive these two in a straight line.' He was enjoying his little joke mightily.

And, strangely, so was I, for there was a quality in John Parker's grin that told me we had crossed a watershed because never once had I blamed the horses.

I did not know it at the time, but the foundations of my later life were being laid as, week by week, I travelled to east Anglia and fell deeper in love with the place, and with the horses, than I could ever have imagined.

FOUR

By the summer of 1983 our first child, Nicholas, had been born and Libby and I were living in a tidy if small Georgian house in Greenwich, enjoying the distant hoot of ships on the river and the morning mists as they rolled down the hill to the River Thames in nearby Greenwich park. It never crossed our minds that we might live anywhere else, certainly not outside London. We'd moved from Notting Hill and that had been upheaval enough, our friends remarking 'how far out we lived.' They had no idea what lay in store. For much of our first year there I was commuting weekly to east Anglia, driving horses, little realising that the infectious nature of that business was to become all consuming. Life would be so much easier if we could acknowledge the importance of these signposts as we passed them. Why do we only recognise them with the benefit of hindsight?

Even though the first series of *In at the Deep End* was still to be completed, producers were already ringing to ask if for the next series I would consider lion taming? An idea, incidentally, which was stepped firmly upon when David Attenborough was asked if he would appear in the film. His sense that times were changing with regard to our appreciation of performing circus animals was somewhat ahead of ours and he said we were crazy and that such things were just about on the verge of becoming disgusting. Even so I think I would have done it, although that is easy to say at this distance. My producer had been to a meeting with the (I think) Chipperfield family who were still touring a pack of tigers around the country, and he came away with the gleeful news that, 'yes, we can put Paul in with some young tigers. They won't hurt him, they'll only be playful. But remember that if one strikes a playful paw towards you, it can still wipe off your face'. I am belatedly grateful for Attenborough's intervention, and went on to the comparative safety of becoming a chef representing the Roux brothers in a cookery competition. Incidentally, the dish I served in the final contest was a shoulder of lamb, having no idea at the time how many sheep were to eventually land on my plate.

A strange thing: around this time I picked up a Sunday newspaper and read a fanciful article about how we should all do away with our lawns and instead plant wild flower meadows. How typical of the times. Long before global warming and other environmental issues were to prey on our senses of guilt, all that seemed of concern in the natural world were the simple, tangible things like butterflies, birds, hedgehogs, wild flowers, and making compost: concepts we could handle, things to which we could offer help by our own efforts. John Seymour's famous book on self sufficiency was on every middle class bookshelf in the land and as a nation we salivated over 'how to sharpen an axe', or 'how to make our own charcoal' and imagined ourselves skinning our own cows to make hides to keep us warm in our caves at night.

It was that absurdly romantic article, *Every Back Garden a Meadow*, together with a little dash of Seymour, which persuaded me that all inner city gardens needed a pasture. I joined the bandwagon and did my bit for nature by turning our little back lawn in Greenwich into a pastoral idyll. I dug it over, rather badly, and sowed the seed bought (naturally) as a newspaper special offer. I felt so proud, and so satisfied, and so good inside myself. But like the real farming days that were to come, these early ones also had an uncertainty to them. I had never grown grass before and I think I expected an easily won rapid flourish of green with a scattering of yellow primroses followed by a violent blooming of white ox-eye daisies, and so on throughout the seasons as the newspaper had promised. Instead, I remember a sea of mud which lay dormant for months as I suffered scornful looks from neighbours who were beginning to regard us as odd – *The Good Life* was the top rated television show around this time and they were suspicious. Such was our feeble knowledge of gardening matters that Libby and I came down to breakfast one April morning and were filled with joy at seeing the new meadow awash with white flowers which we thought must have bloomed overnight. It was an uplifting, inspiring moment, somewhat diminished when we realised it was no more than the fallen blossom from next door's cherry tree. Nothing much became of my meadow, which was as well because I fear the next stage would have been to try and make some hay. I have no idea if that little postage stamp of south London soil ever became a pasture because by the time of our son's first birthday in November, we had fled.

We escaped eastwards, to the Suffolk coast. My appetite for the east of England had been sharpened by those many visits to John Parker's horses. Libby already thought of it as home, having spent chunks of her childhood there. To move there, and actually live there full-time while having London-based media careers was considered an eccentric thing to do back then; to shun all the virtues of city living in favour of fresh air and green spaces was certainly a wayward way of thinking. In fact, it was such an uncommon urge that I remember, in a moment of deep doubt, asking Libby 'would people think we had failed?' The rural living urge had not reached the wider public; indeed the best-selling magazine, *Country Living*, had not even been launched and we had been residing in rural Suffolk for a good few years before I wrote for its first ever issue.

Our nearest town was Saxmundham, a proud if modest market town where cattle were still sold on a Wednesday and where the estate agents' windows offered several Georgian rectories for sale, all of which were sluggish to sell because few could see any value in them. Why would anyone want an old, damp rectory in the countryside back then? By contrast, in the unlikely event of a rectory coming to the market today, there would be a high speed chase by rich newly marrieds with cash stuffed into the boots of their top-of-the-range Audis. They would drive the A12 like it was Le Mans in the hope of securing one of these vast dwellings, which they would then visit for only the three half terms of the year. We shunned that approach, and wouldn't have had the cash to stuff in the boot anyway.

Instead we bought a rambling old farmhouse with a couple of acres of garden and orchard, and five bedrooms, for the same money we got for our two up, two down in Greenwich, and moved in on the eve of Nicholas' first birthday which we celebrated in a dark, damp farmhouse kitchen by sticking a candle on a digestive biscuit and singing Happy Birthday, not blowing out the candle too soon because the heat it gave off was precious. It was mid November. The house smelt damp, the paint was flaking, the cold wind sang through the rafters, the windows did not close, there was no central heating, the Rayburn was an uncertain ally. Welcome to country life.

But I loved it, probably more than Libby who did not drive a car back then and felt imprisonment at times. I relished every aspect of it, though, from the vegetable garden I created (with deep beds which were all the fashion then, again thanks to Seymour) to the glories of the Victorian brickwork in the deep and dark septic tank which lurked at the bottom of the orchard and silently did its mysterious work. Our neighbour was an old farm worker called Will who once shared with me just one of his many secrets of vegetable growing. 'You want to get down into that old septic tank and pull out a bucket full of that liquid in there and put it on your cabbages. Good stuff, that is.' On other horticultural matters he was less forthcoming: I once asked how he grew such plump and juicy onions? 'Nothin' special about growin' onions' was all he would reveal.

I knew from the moment I read the agent's particulars that this was the house for us, and that we would eventually live there, although I have no memory of how we decided to make the move, or what finally drove us to it. Some tidal flow in one's life, I assume. It was an ancient house, added to over the generations, but at heart still a fifteenth century farmhouse painted white with a clay tile roof, and dormer windows that looked out on the heavy clay fields that make Suffolk farmland so rich. Libby always called it her 'mediaeval cave'

I remember the joy of first driving past it, seeing the undulations of its many roofs, the leaded panes on the windows, the solidity of it and a hand of welcome which it seemed to extend. I stopped the car. The owner was working in his picture-book vegetable plot, like Mr McGregor come to life. I asked, as casually as I could, if the house was still for sale? He told me that he was pretty confident it had been sold. I was heartbroken. I returned to London and remember telling Libby, petulantly, that if I could not live there I would not live anywhere, so there. Imagine then, a few weeks later, when the owner made contact to say that the sale had fallen through. Were we still interested?

In many ways it was an amiable, yet at the same time, nightmare of a house. Windows and doors were poor fits and heat leaked out faster than it could be replenished. There was not a right angle of any kind anywhere in its construction, and there was enough damp in the air to fill a bath every night; there were no even floors, and the previous owner warned us that in parts of the house there were 'remnants of an earlier electrical system'. But it had a garden, a small orchard on which I could use all those axe-sharpening lessons Seymour's writings had taught me, and next door was a disused range of farm buildings. These were to prove pivotal in this slowly but inevitably developing story.

At around the time that our daughter, Rose, was born a year later, I set to work to build a dog kennel. Most parents of small children believe they have enough livestock already on their hands, but the arrival of Tim, a top-bred working border collie, was part of the ongoing circus of *In at the Deep End* which was about to film its second series.

'Sheep dog trialling?' my producers asked. Yes please, I replied, without hesitation. This was to be another of the bricks that were to form the foundation of my farming life, for although the horse and carriage driving had brought me out into the countryside, I had yet to discover something that would make me feel as though I was a part of it. So far, I had walked through the scenery and now I wanted to be a real part of the action. My sheep dog trialling efforts were to provide that.

I knew nothing of sheep, and as with all my tasks in that series I was genuinely starting with a blank sheet. I had, of course, seen the hugely popular *One Man and his Dog*, but much of it remained a mystery to me despite the efforts of the commentators, Eric Halsall and Phil Drabble, both of whom I was later to meet. I was to discover it to be a highly competitive world, far worse than horse driving if such a thing were possible. The participants were highly unusual figures. Most were full time shepherds, men of the hills and fells and less often the vales. Some spoke few words, except to their dogs, while others were more forthcoming if amused by my efforts.

The most important thing, I had been told, was that the dog and I must bond, not as dog owners usually do in a kind of mutual friendship; this had to be a master and servant relationship. Tim came from Bedfordshire, from Norman Seamark, one of the top breeders in the country and for hours the two of us motored through the night to Suffolk. We exchanged the odd glance in the driving mirror but our eyes never met for long. I would occasionally ask him how he was, but got only a confused stare in reply. It was early days; we had months in which to get to know each other, and if this first meeting passed without any upsetting incident then that was a good omen. Imagine how he must have felt, though, having been plucked from his secure home and thrust into my inexpert care.

Tim was a fine looking dog. Even the little bit of him that I could see in the driving mirror was endearing. His black,wet nose shone in the passing headlights, his distinctive black and white border collie markings framed his dark face and eyes, and I fancied I could see in them the sorrowful look of an eternal refugee, for that is what he had been for the first seven years of his life. Born in Wales (we thought), brought to Bedfordshire to be trained by the man who was also to train me, and then thrust into the back of the car like a hostage and despatched to Suffolk in order that he and I might 'bond'. Talk about sheepdog trials. Poor old Tim. From the outset I felt as sorry for him as he clearly did for himself.

As guests go, although Tim did not know it, he had little to look forward to. I had been told quite forcibly that he should not be allowed to become a pet; no sight of the roaring fire for Tim but a chain and a kennel in the yard and only a bit of straw to make it home. Every meal would have to be fed from my hand to remind him who was master, every command must be obeyed, and within five months we should both have arrived at a point where we could read each other's mind. Telepathy, I was told, was the shepherd's secret and is the reason why, until they invent the intelligent tractor, there will be no better way of handling sheep than with a sheepdog.

It was late evening when we eventually arrived back home, Tim by now with crossed legs and his nervous new owner with crossed fingers, hoping the dog wasn't going to make a run for it as soon as the car door opened. He leapt out on the end of his stout leather lead and made the first of many territorial marks against the wheel of the car.

I fetched an old length of washing line from the garage so that on his first night he would have limited scope for roaming. I urged him into the kennel, a five star billet compared to some; it had been a child's Wendy house, but this did not impress Tim. He just sat and fixed me with large, watery eyes that shone like motorway markers in the darkness. I left him there to fetch his food and water, and as I walked up the path to the house I watched the two flashes of light follow my every move.

When I came back five minutes later there was no dog. He had gone. The rotten line had parted. I looked in the kennel. No sign. I shouted, 'Tim! ... Tim! ...' But he hardly knew my voice yet. Poor dog. I imagined him to be scampering across the fields in search of his old home two hundred miles away. Or worse: perhaps he'd found some sheep or cattle and started trying to boss them around in the darkness. A farmer might shoot him. I panicked.

Then there was the money. Tim was a highly tuned and trained sheepdog. He had a pedigree which would have put him in the higher echelons of the Royal Family if he had been born human instead of dog. There was a good thousand pounds' worth of border collie roaming around Suffolk, and all I could do was yell, 'Tim!...Tim!' into the night.

'I've found him,' my wife shouted from the other side of the house. The sad little dog was curled up, paw across his muzzle as if to hide from the world, almost asleep on the warm bonnet of the car that had brought him here. Our hearts went out to him and, with no resistance, he returned to his kennel attached to it this time with a length of chain. But he didn't impress easily, and curled up on the cold, damp earth as far away from the kennel as the chain allowed. We went to bed a little fonder of Tim than we ever thought we might be at this early stage in our relationship.

The warm glow of compassion soon faded. It was about three o'clock in the morning when we woke to the sound of a low, distant moan that would occasionally rise to a piercing crescendo. The howl of a wolf? No, the cursed dog. We lived some way off the beaten track so there were few neighbours, but this incessant howling and moaning would wake people in a village a mile away. We wrapped ourselves in dressing gowns and duffel coats and went out into the chill night to tell Tim that everything was alright, and that he should belt up.

It worked, for all of half an hour, and then the ghostly chorus would start up again, moaning and sighing like a storm in the rigging of a sailing ship. In desperation we went to the fridge, took out a large lamb chop and flung it at him from the bedroom window.

It was shortly after, during one of my early training visits to a farm in Bedfordshire that my tutor, Norman Seamark, a top trialist and the time President of the International Sheepdog Society spelt out for the me the proper place of the working animal on a farm, and it is a lesson I have never forgotten for it applies to all working animals, 'A happy and contented dog is a dog that knows what it should be doing and how it should be behaving' And Norman practiced what he preached. In his time he had owned over a score of border collies and not a single one of them had set so much as a paw across his threshold. It was a brave dog that jumped up at Norman, as dogs do, in search of a quick stroke or cuddle, for they will be rebuked with a less than affectionate 'GET down!' And they will get down because they know he means it. But they're happy dogs too. They know their place, and their job. On my first of many training days, Tim rushed towards me and jumped up. I was rather flattered. 'He wants to play,' I said, half joking. 'No,' Norman insisted. 'It might have been play when he was a puppy, but it's now his work of a lifetime. The playing is over.' And clearly for me too.

I spent many weeks in Norman's fields with his sheep, learning the commands, but I was soon to delve deep into a different kind of rural life than I had ever been before when we went to south Wales to meet a champion shepherd, Gwilym Jones.

He had farmed near Llandeilo all his life. Sheep were his work but trialling was his life. His special skill was to work two dogs at once – the brace. That might sound easier than working with one dog, many hands making light work etc, but each dog has to be under individual command and, given that orders to one dog alone can fly around like machine gun bullets, having to give orders to two seems almost impossible. But he was a champion and so was his father before him.

He was a short man and spoke only occasionally with a broad accent, sometimes lapsing into Welsh. He wore a flat cap. There was a row of seven hooks on the wall of the cottage; each carried a flat cap, one for each day of the week, a clean one for Sundays.

'I want you to go and gather those sheep from that field there.' He pointed with his crook to a field that looked empty because of the rise of the land in the middle of it which meant that the sheep grazing at the far end weren't visible from where I was standing.

'And I want you to bring them into this field here.'

And he went away. No advice, no further comment – he just left it to me.

This was all new to me. This wasn't going round in circles in a small field, it was real work. It felt like being a sprinter released from daily training on the track and told to run for a bus. I was a real shepherd! I looked round for Gwilym but he was back at the cottage. Tim and I were on our own.

I called Tim to heel.

'See your sheep,' I whispered, the first command designed to make the dog attentive. Tim tensed.

'Come by,' I said and he ran away to the left, striking out in an enormous arc to gather the sheep, most of whom were out of my sight on the other side of the hill.

Tim raced on till he was out of my sight too. Then I waited. It might have been thirty seconds but it felt like thirty minutes. First one sheep's black face appeared over the brow of the hill, then a dozen more. Not charging but walking steadily towards me. No sign of Tim, just sheep. How many? Perhaps three hundred.

Then I saw half a dozen sheep madly sprinting in the opposite direction through a hedge and into an adjoining field. This was not right. What now? Leave the flock of hundreds to their own devices while I sent Tim off to gather the strays? Would Tim obey, anyway, at that distance? Tim was thinking faster than I was, though, and was already in hot pursuit. The larger flock came to a standstill, having sensed Tim's distraction, and the strays were now coming under his influence. He moved like lightning, displaying to the full his remarkable natural instinct which was to bring the flock of sheep to the feet of his master. The few were gathered together and joined the many, and within a minute I was standing on a Welsh hillside in the middle of a flock of hundreds with Tim darting in every direction keeping them in place at my feet. I was proud of that dog.

Gwilym returned. He didn't say anything. It was a routine manoeuvre to him, but a triumph for me. While we were chatting, Tim wandered off and did a bit of undirected shepherding of his own. 'Look, he's roaming around,' said Gwilym. 'I wouldn't let my dog do that. Keep him at your heel. Look! He's starting to wander again. Keep him there. Don't let him off the hook. Don't let him take a step you don't want him to take.'

They were the wisest of words, and ones which were to echo down through my farming years.

Although I was enjoying the variety of landscapes that the filming of that programme took me to, it was the people that I found the most interesting. Old Gwylym was as much a part of those Welsh hillsides as the grey rock, and Geoff and Viv Billingham who were shepherds on the Duke of Roxburghe's estate were true border people, and shepherds to the core.

Around their kitchen stove, in a wild and remote spot many miles down a lane that leads nowhere, we settled down to a farmhouse tea. Scones, jam, thickly spread bread, strong tea and long tales of the long, hard winters. This was a part of the country where bad weather dominates, where only sheep can thrive, and summer is a mere respite from the frost and snows of the long, harsh winters.

'It's in the winter you feel closest to your dogs,' said Geoff. 'If it weren't for your dogs you'd be on your own. You're out there in a snowstorm and you know you've got to find your sheep. You can't see them but your dog can smell them and he'll take you to them.' A look of pride came over his face. 'Last winter there was a sheep in a ditch and it was completely covered in snow and sinking further and further. But the dog found it and actually got hold of it by the neck wool and was starting to drag it out. You can breed a strain of dog that's almost human.

'That dog will actually know what you're thinking,' added Viv. 'At lambing time, for example, if he sees a ewe in trouble, perhaps the lamb's too big for her or something, he'll automatically stop and look at the ewe, then he'll glance at you as if to say, 'Look! There's a ewe in trouble. Do you want me to catch it?'

'You couldn't be a shepherd without a dog,' said Geoff. 'You get whizz-kids these days who drive around on fast motorbikes and gather up the sheep that way. But they'll never replace the dog. Dogs can use their brains, machines never can.'

The day of my sheepdog trial, which was held in the grounds of Woburn Abbey, eventually arrived. I didn't do a bad job; the sheep were flighty, Tim was strong headed, I didn't have the experience but I achieved the grand climax which was to get all the sheep into the final holding pen. And as I made those final moves which led to the capture of the small flock, the wise words of the shepherds I had met were ringing in my ears.

If you're in a hurry with sheep, take your time ... sheep have only one ambition in life, and that is to die ... some time, long ago, sheep were given a nasty fright and they aren't quite over it yet ...

During the process of learning to work my dog and gather my sheep, I now realise that I had crossed an invisible line, and would forever after that wish to be some sort of countryman. Not because I had fallen for the birds, bees, flowers and trees; but because for the first time in my life I had met country people and found that I understood how they lived and worked, and thought. I found them easy to talk to, and good company. And, strangely for someone who felt he was an outsider when it came to rural life, I found we could

29

talk on equal terms. It was the start of what has turned out to be the most important conversation of my life.

FIVE

Tim the sheep dog returned to the farm from which he came and surprisingly I was not sad to see him go. He had done more than his job. I now understood that a working dog had its place, and that is with its sheep, and at that time I didn't have any. Anyway, I now had enough working animals on my plate. Still recovering from being deeply infected by the world of horse and carriage driving, and with great help and patience from John Parker, I had bought a pair of black Fell ponies, hardy little workhorses, and established them in those old farm buildings next to the house. The moment I'd set eyes on them, I knew those old buildings would have a use.

And now another harsh lesson was being learnt: it's all very well driving horses when you are under the sharp eye of a master like John Parker and the rest of the highly skilled people at his stables, it is another when you are on your own and only have shallow skills and experience to fall back on. There were times when I was reduced to tears by that cunning little mare, Ebony, who had a mind of her own; or her truculent other half, a thick-set, solid-headed kind of a horse, China. But when you are forced to learn it is often surprising how fast

31

it all comes to you, and it was not long before we were sitting atop our carriage and trotting round the east Suffolk lanes as though we were living in the days before the outbreak of the First World War.

A couple of years passed with much time spent grooming ponies, polishing harness, taking visitors for drives, trying to grow onions and cabbages as well as Will did next door. Then, out of the blue, another tremor ran through my life, another portent of things to come, a movement of the ground on which I stood that was to eclipse all others so far and propel me deeper into country life and living than I ever thought it possible to go. As so often happens, it all came about by crazy accident.

The grand Annual Dinner of the *Suffolk Horse Society* brings together a strange mix of men. They come from all parts of Britain, but principally from East Anglia, and over a hot dinner pay homage to a breed of cart-horse: the Suffolk Punch. Some will be remembering their horses as old friends with whom they spent countless hours in days that they recall as happier and more content than any since, but there will be arguments too. The question of which horse could plough the straightest furrow is as much chewed over today as when the disputed furrow was drawn, maybe fifty years ago. A man who achieved his reputation three score or more years back cannot rest in peace either, for, whether it is for the glories of his horsemanship or the stupidity of his ways that he is remembered, his name is sure to pass around the tables at the Annual Dinner.

'I remember that horse ... why, that must have been nineteen thirty ... er ... six that must. I could have led him to that plough and he'd have done the job 'isself. That's true, that is,' an old boy boasted in his broad, sing-song Suffolk accent.

On the table where I was sitting a few legends were being exhumed, like the one about the gallant Suffolk boy who walked to London. He was an apprentice farrier and had just forged a shoe that he thought was second to none. Not a single dent had the repeated blows of his hammer left on it: it was like a mirror. Seeking a wider stage on which to boast than that which the village forge could provide, he slipped the shoe in his pocket and walked to Crystal Palace, where his magnificent horse-shoe became the centre-piece of the Great Exhibition.

'That's true, that is,' said Roger Clark, a farmer who was sitting opposite me. He had just emerged from another long and involved tale with Hector, a farrier, who was sitting on my left. If I had understood the tale I would gladly re-tell it, but as the discussion became heated so the accent grew thicker and I had to be content with understanding one word in ten. However, I did gather that the dispute centred around the way a horse had been shod and, 'That should never have been, that shouldn't!' I waited some time for a pause and got in quick with a question.

'When was all this?' I asked. They both looked up, silently. Quick sums were being done in their heads.

'Must have been about nineteen ... twenty ... five.' And they both looked down at their plates and quietly tucked in. The long-running annual debate had been held and honour satisfied on all sides.

'What you've got to understand,' said Roger, 'is that there was no one prouder of his horses than a horseman on a farm. It didn't matter if they was going in the show-ring or coming back down the lane after a hard day's work, a horseman worthy of the name wanted his horses lookin' better than them next door.' At which point the chairman banged the table to call the room to order, and the engraved silver cups were awarded. Actually, Roger Clark was called to the rostrum to collect nearly all of them; for not only is he a farmer and farrier, he is also a highly respected and consistently successful exhibitor of Suffolk horses.

I could not make him out, to start with. His eyes fell easily into a distant stare, the stare of a man who is used to looking ahead as he follows a plough. Although he was then only forty and could have little memory of the days when only the Suffolk horse tilled the Suffolk land, his working knowledge of horse-drawn cultivation seemed remarkably detailed. I knew he was an eminent farrier, a Fellow of the *Worshipful Company of Farriers* and reckoned to be at the very top of his profession ('I can tack a horseshoe on a fingernail, if I have to,' he once told a customer who thought a horse had got problem feet), but I sensed that there was more to him even than that, so I gathered up all my courage and quizzed his then wife, who I had heard was a formidable lady.

Cheryl Clark (now Grover) is short in body but immense in strength and courage, and in will-power too. She first met Roger at the Woodbridge Horse Show twenty years ago and defied her father to marry him. She took up her husband's trade and qualified as a farrier; she rides and hunts, but above all she breaks heavy horses to harness – no horse has ever broken her. She sports muscular arms that a grown man would be proud of. Her vocal range is impressive, both in the distance it can carry and the pitch to which it can rise. It is easy to see how one piercing word from Cheryl would crush the most truculent of animals.

She described her household. 'We've got six Suffolks at home in full-time work, and then we have others coming in for breaking. I've got two more Suffolks I'm breaking in and a couple of Shires, and I've got a couple of Percherons coming in before Christmas.' She spoke as if having in her charge six untamed horses, each weighing over a ton, was a matter of course.

'Naturally, we make our Suffolks work,' she announced.

I wasn't quite clear what she meant. She went on, 'They don't just stand around looking pretty. They have to work for their living.' How? 'On the farm, of course,' she said, as if this was too obvious to be worth saying. 'We ain't got no tractors, just hosses!' If I'd had ears like a horse, they would have been pointing sharply forwards at this. I listened as she told me about the sowing and ploughing and the horse-drawn harvesting. She told me about the hundred-plus acres that they farmed as tenants on one of the large Suffolk estates; and about the mangel-wurzels and the kale and tares, the ducks and geese in the yard, the fattening pig in the sty.

'The horses plough the land, they pull the drill that sows the seed and then they eat what they've grown. The horses eat the mangels, the sheep eat the tares.'

She might have been describing a family farm of the 1920s, or, I suppose, of any time up to the Second World War; not one that you would expect to flourish in Suffolk in what were then the late 1980s.

It became clear to me what set the Clarks apart from the rest. I resolved all the questions about them that were in my mind. They were not living in the past like so many other farmers at this dinner who praised the glories of the Suffolk horse while back home the tractors rumbled relentlessly across their land. Nor were they self-appointed protectors of an endangered species who might take an animal like a Suffolk horse and only parade it in public, never allowing it to fulfil its sole reason for being on earth, which is to work for its living. The Clarks have built their lives around their love of the Suffolk horse, and in return have given the horse what it needs most: land to plough and sow and reap. It is a circle of contentment.

I decided, across that dinner table, that I wanted to join in. Not only to satisfy a journalist's curiosity about the working horse and this bygone slice of rural life, but because I too was brought up on farmyard stories of the speckled-hen, Dobbin the carthorse, Daisy the milk-provider and tales of cross old Farmer Brown. For selfish, and undeniable romantic, reasons, at the age of thirty-eight, I wanted to be a farmer's boy.

And where might such an idea have come from? You now know as much about my roots as I do and I think you would agree that there is little to suggest that it would be a farmer's life for me. But perhaps these things come not in tidal waves but in small ripples, and I suppose they had been growing for some time; in the back garden in Greenwich, on the carriage seat behind the horses, in my garden, with the shepherds and their sheep. Certainly something quite cataclysmic was happening and I remember that when the idea of being a farmer first crossed my mind, it was an all-consuming experience on a par with what I imagine a religious experience to be. There was nothing else I wanted to be, nothing else I wanted to do in my life.

And so I set off one Sunday morning in late November, a month after that dinner, with the intention of persuading the Clarks to take me on as a farm-hand and labourer, one day a week for a year, so that I could grasp what might be a last chance to learn to farm with horses. I had no knowledge of agriculture and only a recent contact with horses: light horses, of course, not 'heavies' like Suffolks. But by the end of the year I wanted to be able to call myself a horseman. More importantly, I wanted the Clarks to think of me as a horseman as well. I wanted to have followed the plough and the binder, and to have reaped what I had sown.

Their farm, Weylands Farm, is 117 acres of south Suffolk and it took some finding. I approached down a gravel track having taken a turn off the A12 somewhere near a sign marked 'Constable Country'. I paused before pulling into the yard. To the left, the land gently sloped away to meet a river I had just crossed. A handful of sheep were grazing some hard patch of stubbly earth, working hard to get their teeth round the remnants of some greenery that was poking through the soil. A little further on was a muck-heap. Not a tip, or a dump, but a heap; something that had been constructed rather than thrown together. It steamed.

No sight of a farmhouse yet, nor any horses. I paused again alongside the muck-heap to take in the view and the smell, both of which were impressive. Fields here were smaller than is usual on the large-scale farms of the 1980s, and handfuls of woodland remained intact. Animals grazed. Not huge herds, but five or six cattle in one field, a couple of dozen sheep in another and a squealing crush of pigs in a filthy little midden of their own making tucked away in a corner. Some of the more distant fields had been marked out with what looked like a single furrow made by one pass of a plough and left, as if a linesman had started to mark out a football pitch and run out of paint.

The land turned sharply to the right and the farmstead came out of hiding. It stood open only to the south, the least malicious of directions from which the winter wind can blow. For shelter the house backs on to hills, so that although it might look from a distance as though it had been thoughtlessly perched on that hillside, it was in fact cosily cocooned on three sides.

It looked like a child's drawing of a farmhouse: white walls with a door in the middle and windows spaced symmetrically on either side. The roof was of bright red pan-tiles with a brick chimney-stack slap in the middle of it, billowing black smoke. There was no path to the front door (there never is in East Anglian farmhouses: front doors are traditionally for weddings or funerals) so I went round the other side and found that the back door, with more yapping terriers standing guard than I could count, opened on to the farmyard itself. It had been a wet autumn, and so the yard was six inches deep in places with glutinous, boot-gripping mud. An arsenal of farm machinery was lined up: carts stood next to aged contraptions heavy with chains and cogs, which managed by their complexity to conceal what work they did. None had an engine. But still I saw no horses.

The back door opened and a hunched figure stumbled out. His flat cap was well down over his forehead, and as he fumbled to deposit an empty beer bottle in the inner lining of his tired blue coat it was impossible to guess if he was a fifty-year-old who had had a hard life, or an eighty-year-old who was doing well for his age. He shuffled off in his wellington boots and I guessed he was probably a grand old gentleman of the land.

It was the middle of the day, dinner-time on the farm. Roger sat at the head of the table in the small kitchen, his back to an aged but serviceable coke-fired boiler. Bottles of horse medicine and veterinary books were littered around, a shotgun was propped in the corner. Doorsteps of toasted cheese were landing on the table with brisk regularity. The door to the sitting room was ajar and I could see an array of silver trophies on a sideboard. Cheryl sat next to Roger, glued to the weekly farming programme on the television. A shiny twelve-wheeled harvester flashed across the screen, proudly showing its ability to crunch up so many acres of something or other per hour.

'Look what them wheels is doing to that land!' screamed Cheryl, voice instantly engaged in high gear. 'That land will be ruined, that will be. You wouldn't get horses' feet chewing up land like that.' She shook her head in disbelief. The commentator mentioned the many tens of thousands of pounds that this machine cost. Roger dropped his fork and leaned back in his chair.

'I could buy a fair few old hosses for that money,' and we laughed.

I explained my mission. I told them how I wanted to come and work here, one day a week for a year. Cheryl smiled.

'So, you want to come and work with us, do you?' She was enjoying every letter of the word 'work' as she twisted it around before spitting it out. I asked where the horses were, the famous Clarks' Punches.

'Always turned out in the meadows on a Sunday. They work hard the rest of the week,' said Roger.

'I give 'em a bloody good physic on Sunday morning,' added

Cheryl, and explained the laxative properties of a good bran mash and how it revitalised the jaded horses.

'I'll just join in and do any jobs that need doing with horses or anything else,' I said humbly, trying to steer the conversation back to my odd request. On the screen, the motorbike revved and screamed, flinging mud to either side as it careered around the countryside.

'That's rubbish what he says,' screamed Cheryl. I froze. She pointed at the screen. 'He says that that machine's the only thing that could get them places. A horse could.' God help the hapless salesman who turned up here trying to flog a tractor.

'Fridays and Mondays are the best days,' said Roger.

I begged his pardon.

'Fridays or Mondays are best if you want to come and work with us,' he repeated.

I realised I had got myself a job.

SIX

It took me very little time to adapt to the pace of farm work for, as I had already learned, it is dictated by the speed of the horse which seemed to be a natural pace at which to work. In the early days I would sprint up the slippery path to the cattle pen to deliver the early morning feed, clutching a heavy sack or bucket of corn; but within a few weeks I learnt that anything other than a measured pace was a waste of effort. A hasty pace forward meant an equally speedy slither backwards; so I learned to take it slowly and get there just as quickly, the philosophy of a true landsman. In those dormant days of winter, I cannot remember feeling any sense of urgency except when the morning tea-break was approaching. Then we would not want to be far from the house in case we failed to hear the call.

Having made all these personal adjustments of pace, both in mind and body, I easily became resentful about intrusions into the timelessness of the place. I found that the approaching rattle of a diesel engine, heralding more horses for shoeing, became an irritation. They hissed their brakes and revved their engines as they manoeuvred in the yard. Some were as big as long-distance coaches, and when they had finally switched off the engines the blaring stereos continued to obliterate the silence. I would give the drivers a scornful look, as you might at a man who was playing a radio in church.

I wonder what the horses thought of it all? Prince would stand, motionless and obedient as ever between the shafts of his tumbrel having been told to 'stand still, hoss', while out of these luxuriously appointed mobile horse-homes would gaily trip ballerina-like thoroughbreds and spirited showjumpers; flighty gymnasts descending into the midst of heavyweight boxers. Some would rear and plunge as they came down the ramp, others would need two men pulling on each side to get them back up it again. And Prince would still be standing, not moving an inch. All he would need would be a 'guurtt on, hoss' and he would ease his mighty shoulders into the collar, the leather would creak, the chains scrape as they went taut, and the muck-cart would make its way back up the hill. From the horsebox came the sounds of nervous dancing as these unsure visitors pranced impatiently on the spot. 'A dreadful waste of energy,' Prince must have been thinking to himself.

Apart from being an agricultural backwater, Weylands Farm was also a cultural centre. Those whose hearts reposed in days gone by came here for spiritual refreshment, or simply to share the like-minded company.

It was the visit from the hairdresser that had attracted the local wart-charmer, and elderly but bright-eyed man called Claude who sat in silence while his thin silver hair was trimmed. In fact, I cannot remember him saying one word all the time he was there. I don't even think he bothered with a goodbye – unusual for him, so they said. Only later, over the dinner table, was the breadth of this man's talents revealed. Roger told the story with great relish, for Roger with a good tale is a sight to behold. He will lean back in his chair, then a smile, prompted by a recollection in his mind, will cross his face and he will stare out of the window as he tells it.

'I was down at Claude's the other day. He dresses pheasants, you know. Well, I went into his front room and there was a dozen of 'em, all lying round the edge of his dining table with their heads hanging over the side. There was blood dripping from 'em. He'd put little tin trays underneath to catch the blood, he 'ad. That's true, that is!' and he chortled in disbelief at his own story. I waited.

'Well, he was sitting there in his old armchair with a pheasant on his knee, feathers flying everywhere and his sleeves rolled up and 'e'd got rags round his wrists soaked in paraffin. I said, "What yer got them rags for, Claude?" He says, "To keep them bloody lice from running up m' arms and going over m' head like a gang of harrows." He bloody well had, too! Them old birds, they were lousy as cuckoos, lousy as cuckoos they were.' Roger laughed ever louder. 'I said, "Why you plucking them buggers, them's as rotten as hell?" He said, " 'Cos her at house wants 'em plucked, that's why!"' We laughed. 'But that old devil, he can charm warts, you know.'

I looked at Roger, and there must have been a hint of scepticism flash across my face. He leaned back in his chair. We were in for another cracking tale.

'We had a horse here. That had a big wart on its neck size of a saucer, that must 'ave bin. Size of a saucer! Great big thing it was. Well, that horse, that had been to Newmarket to have tests and God knows how many vets had taken bits here and there but that wart, that just wouldn't budge. Well, old Claude, he was here having his hair cut and this horse came in for shoeing. I said, "You jus' go an' 'ave a look at that there wart." Well, he went out, looked at it for a bit and said, "I can't promus nuthin, but I'll do mar best."'

'Did he touch it?' I asked.

'No,' said Roger. 'He just looked at it, and do you know ...' everyone in the kitchen, even though they must have heard this tale a dozen times before, went silent with attention '... that wart was gone in three weeks.' We all shook our heads.

'Now, we don't know how he does it, but I've heard that these old boys go home and they bury a lump of meat and do something to it, I don't know what. But you mustn't ask, 'cos if they tell you how they does it, then their power passes to you.'

February was a tantalising month. The ground would freeze hard for days on end, and then the wind would swing from the chilling east into the milder and damper west. As soon as the thaw spread through the soil, the land would cry out for work to be done. Then the ice and snow would return and portents of an early spring would vanish once again.

By the end of January there were still fifteen or more acres to plough in parts of the farm I had not yet even seen. Ploughing is a fundamental act, and dangerously and misleadingly picturesque. The thought of it can bring a sentimental glow to the townie's heart, but real-life execution of it brings something more like tears of pain to those, like me, who are new to the ways of this basic and elemental piece of farm equipment they call the plough.

Ploughs lay scattered around Weylands Farm, a dozen at least, mostly blue and recently painted, but some just rusty. They would stand at the end of an abandoned furrow high on a hillside as if, for some calamitous reason, the ploughman had had to flee the field with his horses. The real reason is much less sinister: ploughs are simply left where the day's work ends, and from that point the following day's work will start, if the weather allows.

Rupert and Thomas were in plough harness. Thomas was Roger's best and favourite ploughing horse who usually ploughed alongside Toby, but it was old Rupert's turn today. Plough harness has no saddle to put across the horse's back, since ploughing is pulling rather than carrying work: all that is needed is the stout padded leather collar and a pair of long chains which will eventually hook the two horses to the plough. A light strap goes across the horse's back simply to stop the chains scraping along the ground. Cart-horses seem so much easier to deal with than spirited light horses, and so much less unpredictable in their ways, that one is forced to the conclusion that they are more intelligent. It would be a brave man who would lead a pair of light horses alone on the end of one lead, but with Suffolks this did not feel at all a risky business.

Roger clipped a light chain from Rupert's bit to a ring at the back of Thomas's harness. This simple but highly effective device means that the horses will walk together as an easily controllable pair. If Thomas slows down, the pull on Rupert's bit will slow him too. If, on the other hand, Rupert wants to get a move on, he can speed Thomas up by a good tug. All Roger had to do was walk in front, showing the way and occasionally urging them on up the steepish hill that led to one of the highest fields.

'I wouldn't give that hoss to a boy,' said Roger, pointing towards Thomas as we walked. 'He can be difficult, he can.'

There seemed to be two classes of worker on a farm: horsemen and boys. Boys might be in charge of a pliable horse, the sort you would put between the shafts of a muck-cart. Horsemen were needed to exert their authority over horses like Thomas. Indeed, horsemen were the crown princes on farms in the days when horses ruled. The 'guv'nor' was the farmer or landowner for whom they all worked, but the head horseman was not far behind in the pecking order, even though he was an employee, and he had distinct rights of precedence over all other horse-men. It would be his sole privilege to be first to leave the stable yard when more than one team of horses went out to plough. Equally, it would be his word that would be law when it came to working the horses on the fields.

'The best way to learn to plough is on a snowy day,' said Roger. 'You don't need any horses. Just set up a stick at the other end of a field and walk towards it in as straight a line as you can. When you get to the stick, look back and see how straight your path was. You can't plough straight if you can't walk straight.'

The aged plough was made by Ransomes, a famous Suffolk manufacturer of farm machinery and their name was stamped proudly down the two handles. There were two wheels at the front, one larger and one quite small: one to run in the furrow, the other to run higher on the unploughed land. Moving backwards along the length of the plough, next came a short spade-like affair called a 'skimmer' which runs along the surface of the unploughed land, scraping off a thin layer of stubble or weed and throwing it to one side so that it is covered with soil and buried when the plough pours a slice of earth over it. Then came the 'coulter'. This is a vertical knife which cuts the upright side of the slice of earth that the plough is to turn over. Then, a couple of inches behind, the leading edge of the mould-board, the wave-shaped piece of cast iron which actually turns the earth. The tip of this is the hard iron 'plough-share' itself, and this cuts horizontally before curving upwards, so that, together with the coulter, a block of earth is first cut before the mould-board comes slithering along to turn it over.

'Stand there, hoss,' ordered Roger. Not shouted or barked but merely stated, and the horses obeyed and stood by the head of the plough and gazed into the far distance, or as much of it as their blinkers allowed them to see. Roger strode off to the far end of the field and the horses watched. Until he gave another command, they would not move; in the minutes that he was away, not one muscle flinched except for the heaving of their mighty chests, still puffing after the long climb up the hill.

Roger returned with a stick with a white rag tied round the top of it. Then he paced and counted to himself as he walked, stopped when he reached some magic number and then decisively rammed the stick into the ground. Then he strode back to the far end of the field and once again counted the same number of paces from the last furrow that had been ploughed, and rammed another stick into the earth. Then he came back to where the horses and I were standing, rapt. More gulls were gathering in anticipation.

The drawing of the first furrow on a new piece of land has always been a sacramental task. It was never delegated nor undertaken lightly, for a head horseman's reputation would depend on it. A man who could not plough a straight furrow was a man who counted for nothing. You were as good as your furrow, and if it was less than perfect it was an enduring shame: nothing could conceal the meandering of the plough and it would be there for all to see till young green growth concealed it – one season of shame.

So, with the reputation of generations of ploughmen weighing heavily on his shoulders, and with concentration that would do justice to Euclid scribing a line, Roger set his horses along the line of the two sticks. He spoke quietly, like a man whose mind was totally occupied.

'In them old ploughing matches, you know, those boys, they used to go out there and draw a furrow, and they reckon that if that deviated more than seven-tenths of an inch in its whole length, that weren't no good.'

'G'up,' called Roger and, as if by some faultless remote control, the two horses took up the drag of the plough on their huge collars and set off down the imaginary line between the two sticks that was about to become the first furrow.

'Walk behind me,' called Roger. 'If you walk alongside you'll catch my eye and distract me.' As soon as the plough had bitten the earth the furrow started to take shape. I stepped into it and, like any jolly fellow, I followed the plough.

This was sandy land, not the hard, unyielding clay for which parts of Suffolk are famous, and so the plough bit easily. It scythed through the ground, the soil swished with the crash of a wave, and turned over a perfect slice of earth. Like the mesmerising wake of a ship, or the vapour trail of a high-flying plane, it had to be watched in case, during a glance away, it might change its perfect form. Stones were cast aside as easily as earth, and the swooshing noise was occasionally broken by a sharp ring as a stone hit the plough-share. And the horses marched on, unguided by voice or hand.

Following in the furrow was not as easy a stroll as I expected. It is not quite wide enough to walk with each foot side by side, and so one foot is in the depths of the furrow while the other is on the heights of the unploughed land. It means that you have to watch where you're treading, and I found this frustrating when all I wanted to watch was the plough and the horses. The horses themselves seemed to manage their feet quite easily, though.

'Cup, cup,' muttered Roger, the order to his horses to move to the left: no more than that, no pull on the rope.

'Woooahh,' he called softly as we reached the far stick, and the horses stopped in unison. Roger looked back and gave his furrow a long hard stare. It was white now down all its length with screaming, ravenous gulls. I had been concentrating so hard that I had not heard them descend, even though they must have flocked on to the ground the instant the plough had turned it over.

The furrow was as straight as my eye could detect. 'That's not too bad,' was as far as Roger would allow himself to go, and then for the first time he took hold of the rope and gave the horses a guiding tug. 'Wheesh … wheesh …' he urged them, and they side-stepped to the right until they were pointing in the opposite direction, but still standing on the same spot. As they turned, Roger chose his moment and put his weight on the handles so that the plough lifted from the soil; he guided it round so that most of its huge weight was carried round by its own momentum. Get the timing wrong and you would have the whole mass of the iron plough on your hands and 180 degrees through which to turn.

Roger talked of 'splitting' and 'shutting up' and described circles in the air as he tried to explain how the first furrow was then ploughed again, and then again down either side till it became a 'top' and then the ploughman would go in circles round that till it had been 'shut up' to the adjacent stretch. I was lost, so I watched and listened and hoped that I would eventually understand.

'You shouldn't have to fight the plough at all. That plough, that should go on its own if you let go of the handles.'

'G'up,' and we marched on. Then we stopped. Roger made comparisons with the previous furrows and took the spanner to the plough with as much delicacy as a mechanic tuning up a six-cylinder engine. There was never any suggestion of a 'that would do' approach. Either a furrow had been drawn properly or it hadn't, and if the second was not parallel to the first there would be no use shrugging it off, for it was sure to catch up with you. When one stretch met the next, that was the moment of truth. It is not unlike the wallpapering of a room. If the first piece isn't upright, the last piece isn't going to be.

'Them furrows have got to be level too or that seed won't all be buried at the same depth and you'll get some bits ripening before others, and we don't want that. Do you want a go?'

I was offered the plough and we slithered on our way. The plough bit into the earth and I watched the furrow-wheel with such intent that I did not have a chance to work out where my feet were falling. Walking in the furrow thus ceased to be a problem; my feet did the thinking for me. 'Just press on the handles and steer it, don't fight it, just guide it. Cup, cup ... Thomas. Gurt on, hoss!'

'That's not too bad,' said Roger, 'but that's a hard job to get your work just right,' and he kicked loose earth over the foot of land where my plough had jumped out of the furrow. He couldn't bear the sight of even a tiny mistake in his beautifully ploughed field.

Then I ploughed some more while Roger guided the horse, and after a couple of 'rounds' or circuits of the stretch I was able to relax and enjoy the crash of the earth as if fell away from the plough and the precision with which the horses' feet fell exactly into the furrow: a mark of a true and well-bred Suffolk horse.

'That must be gettin' near four o'clock,' said Roger. 'That old hoss, he's gettin' awkward. He don't like to plough much after four o'clock. That's his regular feed-time.' And as he spoke, Cheryl appeared over the brow of the hill clutching Thermos flasks of tea. She looked cold, almost frost-bitten.

'I've been sitting in that meadow with an old ewe who didn't look too well. I thought she might be havin' a bit of bother with her lamb but she's getting' on all right,' and she rubbed her hands to warm them. We all felt the chill now. The wind was settled in the north and the sky was filling with grey cloud that looked laden with snow. The sun was gone. Rupert and Thomas munched a handful of grass that Roger had picked for them and we supped our tea and gazed out over the modest patch of land that we had ploughed. For the first time it crossed my mind that to be atop a Suffolk hill, behind a horse-drawn plough, was as near to total peace as a man might wish to be.

It is only when things go wrong that you realise that the horses have minds of their own, otherwise you can come to think of them as remotely controlled machines. I cannot remember exactly what happened, but my eye was following a flock of rowdy and aggressive gulls who were drawn to the worms that the ploughing brought to the surface of the soil. The field had been littered with them ever since we arrived, but this flock seemed noisier and more boisterous than the rest. I followed them with my eye across the field, and saw them come up behind Roger's three-horse team. I heard Roger cry 'whooah' with much more force than usual, but this time the horses did not respond. They started to bolt, breaking into a trot with the plough still trailing behind them. Cheryl stopped her horses and ran to help. Then Richard fell, dropped like a stone, and that brought the other two horses to a standstill. As he tried to get back on his feet he started to kick out at the others while Roger and Cheryl struggled to free him from the plough. They calmed him with words, and soon he was standing with no apparent damage done.

'He's swoundered,' said Cheryl, 'swoundered hisself.'

Gerry looked on. 'Do you say he swoundered?' he asked.

'When the horse in the middle lunges forward and the other two don't go with him,' Cheryl explained, 'the collar squashes his windpipe and he faints. That's why he fell.'

He was fine within a minute, they hooked him back into the plough, and five minutes later it was as if nothing had happened.

'Did she say he swoundered?' asked Gerry for possibly the third time. I told him he had, and he lit another tobacco-stained slice of paper in celebration of his witnessing a rare phenomenon.

We had our meal break on the headland in the drizzle. Mild rain dripped off our caps into the thick vegetable soup we had brought with us in flasks, and we sat on the empty bean-seed sacks and gorged our sandwiches to satisfy a ravenous appetite while the horses just stood, their backs to the wind.

'I used to borrow other people's fields to start with,' Roger told me, 'and I just learnt to plough that way. Then I went to a few ploughing matches and got to know how to do it over the years. I should say the secret's in the plough. I could give you my plough now and you could go out there and make a decent job of it, but that's because I've set it up. If you had to set it up yourself you could get into a muddle. Setting the plough's the secret,' and he wandered off, distracted by another rabbit hole down which he might set a ferret.

SEVEN

Spring was already spreading to the corners of Weylands Farm. I arrived one day to find Gerry sniffing the air. He seemed to have more sniffing time on his hands now that he only had to press a button to get his mangels ground, instead of flinging himself at the mechanical grinder – electricity had at last found its way into the barn. It was a shame in some ways. There was a knack to turning that machine by hand, mostly in knowing the moment to let go otherwise the momentum of the whole thing could carry you round with it. Such wisdom would presumably now be lost for ever.

'That's a good growing day,' Gerry declared, gazing skyward and sniffing some more. I asked why. 'Cos that ain't too hot and not too wet, and not so dry either. Just a good growing day.' I was none the wiser but wisdom, held in great reserves somewhere within Gerry, did not often surface.

'When I was a boy,' he mused, looking at the dwindling heap of uncut mangel, 'we used to go down the pub, drink beer all night and we'd end up drinking half pints of mangel wine.' His face cracked into a broad grin. 'Bloody rough that was. Christ, you felt dreadful the next morning.' Hangovers were milestones in Gerry's life, each to be remembered and recollected with affection.

We fed the cattle that morning, and having throughout the winter been in the habit of leaving the gate ajar, we did so again. One wilful cow saw her chance and was through; she had to be herded back by a combination of heavy stick and yapping dog.

'They can smell that old grass comin' up,' said Roger. 'Old,' I might add, is a word that has nothing to do with age: we might gather up 'them old lambs' or 'tie up that old fencing' if we felt reasonably disposed to either. The opposite of 'old' is 'bloody', so a cow that had escaped from the field in search of fresh grass was being admired for her cunning if she was 'that old cow, she got out...' But if she had simply been making trouble for all concerned, she was a 'bloody cow that got out'.

I could tell that work had been proceeding well since my last visit by the shine on the normally dull and rusty plough chains. The glint on the inside of the tight links was a sure sign that much heaving and pulling had been done in the previous week, and when I collared Prince and put him to the tumbrel I thought I could see a weary look in his eye which suggested that he had spent many hours between those shafts in the last few days. I still approached the whole business of 'collaring' a horse with some nervousness. The size of them still held me in some awe. I knew deep down that Prince had had his harness on and off his back a couple of thousand times in his life and never flinched. But what if he took exception this time? What if he felt the collar sliding back over his ears and decided his mid-life crisis was due, and went wild? I would stand no chance, sandwiched between his one-ton bulk and the brick wall. I didn't let the worry spoil the pleasure, but it was always in the back of my mind.

And then I arrived one day to be told that Gerry had left.

I was astonished. The farm without Gerry was like a drama with a leading character missing. His unexplained departure meant that new, heavy responsibilities fell upon my inexperienced shoulders. It was all very well to have charge of a horse knowing that a man with fifty years' experience was just round the corner to get you out of any trouble; it was another to be told to get a horse into plough chains and bring him down to such and such a field, knowing that every step it took was a direct consequence of your actions. I felt sure that in my muddled efforts I would miss some vital link of either leather or chain which would mean that the long trudge to the field would soon be followed by a hasty and shaming sprint back to the harness-room. I remember thinking that the plough line would be an easy thing to forget. Because it is neither made of leather, nor jangles like chain, it would be easy to leave it behind in the rush to collar-up and get to work. But to turn up on a field with a pair of harnessed horses and no plough line was as much use as building a fire and forgetting the match. So I checked, and checked again, every time.

Roger had just finished sowing kale, a leafy green fodder crop. 'Put Rupert in that flat roller and just roll that all flat,' he said. 'Up and down and then once or twice round the headland.' And he was off.

This was a turning point: the first time I had been trusted, alone, with a horse, in a field with a real job of work to do. It might not have been the most vital job on the farm, but it had to be done. It was real work, it mattered. Straight lines were paramount, especially as the field was in full view of the kitchen window and any irregularities would surely be remarked upon.

I led Rupert the length of the field, dragging the roller behind, muttering words of encouragement as we went. At the end I looked back. The flattened earth we had just created made a weaving, wandering path. A crippled drunk could have walked straighter. As the outside edge would be part of the headland, I could smooth that out with the final circuit of the roller, but as for the other edge, I would have to overlap and try to do better the next time. So off we trundled in the other direction.

The field was on a hillside and the roller slid, so instead of rolling a path of land parallel to the first, we ended up with a wedge ending in what was almost a point. So that had to be overlapped. It became clear that if each strip was to be corrected like this, it was going to take at least three or four times as long as it should. These deep geometrical thoughts occupied my mind to the extent that Rupert's further meanderings went unnoticed by me, and unchecked, and our next rolled path had an outline like the blade of an abused bread-knife.

It wasn't till the next pass of the roller that I discovered the solution to all my problems. It was quite simple really; all I had to do was let Rupert get on with the job. I had been driving him, whereas he only needed leading. Instead of guiding every one of his footfalls, all I needed to do was to set him in the right direction and offer an occasional correction. When it came to the business of walking in a straight line, Rupert had far more experience than I did. This discovery having been made, I went back to the top of the field and started again, glancing over my shoulder to check that Roger and Cheryl were not watching and thoroughly enjoying themselves at my expense.

When the job was finished, I proudly unhitched Rupert from the roller and walked him back to the barn, rehearsing as I walked what had to be done to put the horse away properly so that the next time I came to the farm an irate Cheryl would not be waiting with a scolding on her lips. I had to unhook the bit from Rupert's mouth ... let him drink water ... walk him to the barn ... take off the harness. Second nature to the Clarks, routine to be learned for me.

I looked behind me to see the results of the afternoon's labours on the rolled field. I could see only the kinks, the waverings of the roller and even an odd triangle of unrolled land. It looked worse as the sun sank and threw crazy shadows which emphasised every undulation. But a true artist is always the most critical of his work, so I hoped it didn't look too bad to a casual observer's eye. Back in the house, over a cup of tea, Cheryl asked Roger which horse I'd been using. Roger told her it was Rupert.

'Rupert,' she muttered. 'Hoss could have done that on his own!'

The cuckoo is the first sign of spring, the swallow a portent of summer. Then Gerry returned, staggering across the yard as if he had never been away. I didn't know whether I was pleased to see him or not. I had enjoyed my fling of solo responsibility, and I knew that now the 'old warrior' had returned I would have to bend to his unalterable will.

Roger asked us to fetch the binder, a sure sign that harvest was on his mind, but the nights grew cold and crisp under clearing skies and northerly winds. Central parts of England were reported to have had ground frosts, and this was the first week in August. Torrential rain beat the land and the standing corn; acre after acre was flattened as if rolled by a massive weight. Grudgingly, that lousy summer eventually gave us a fine day. Reasonably fine, anyway. Clouds threatened, but the air was mild and the breeze gentle, so of all the poor days to try and harvest the rye, Roger judged this to be the most promising – or the least bad. Gerry got a rusty old file out of the forge and started to sharpen the knife of the binder.

But God, how slowly he did it. Each rasp of the file was made as slowly as if he had been polishing some fragile jewel. The clouds gathered and I feared another downpour. Feared, because as a one-day-a-week-farm-worker with only a small field of rye to cut, I might well miss harvest altogether. A horse-drawn farming year without a horse-drawn harvest would be no farming year at all. You might as well turn back from Everest with only a hundred feet to go, or walk from John o'Groats and not bother to go any further than Penzance. Mentally I urged Gerry on, and Roger too.

'That's got to be put together in the right order,' he shouted from the forge. He was bellowing at Gerry who was about to take a hefty spanner to a seized-up wheel of the binder. Roger strode over. He unbolted a wheel here, wound up another and turned a handle, which brought a fleeting burst of life into the machine. Satisfied, he then hitched it to three horses and directed us up the hill to the field of rye.

Even though we were mobile, it was still no clearer how the binder worked, or even in which direction it would go, for in its present configuration the horses were in line with the knife but in front of it, so that any forward motion of the machine was not going to do any cutting, the knife would simply slither through the corn. I hoped things would become clearer.

With one mighty wrench of a rusty spanner and a heave at two of the wheels, the binder revealed itself in its true colours. The bushel under which it had been hiding its light was lifted when I realised that the two wheels at the back were solely to transport the thing along the road. With those removed and the horses swung through ninety degrees, the whole apparatus became recognisable as the subject of countless harvest paintings of the first thirty years of the 20th century, with the horses striding out in front, the driver perched atop, and the wooden sails crashing down on to the upright corn, scooping it into the cutter. After due processing, it should emerge in sheaves or tight bundles, ready to stand and dry in the blazing hot sun.

'Ease up ... ease up a bit ...' 'G'up'. Roger wanted them to feel the strain in their collars before they put their full weight into it.

The binder crept forward and clattered into life.

'Swish!' and the sails came down on to the rye, slashing it and driving it into the frenzied teeth of the cutter. Pushed into the binder by the next sail, it was dragged along a canvas sheet, and then through ninety degrees and upwards. More and more of it was squeezed together when it reached the summit of its climb, until a spring gave, at which point, by some process which a million words could not describe, a greasy device threw a length of twine round the bundle, cut it just above the knot and spat it out on to the ground. True magic. (I later read that the knotter had been invented by a Canadian who was so perplexed by what he had created that his lack of understanding of it forced him to commit suicide.) Behind us was a row of sheaves, tied and tossed aside, and an avenue of spiky stubble.

We had not spat out more than a dozen sheaves when we ground to a cursing halt. So dense and thick were the stalks of rye, and so close were we to the hedges, that the binder could not scoop it up quickly enough at one end, nor eject the sheaves quickly enough from the other. Then the mysterious knotter failed on one or two occasions and we were left with untied sheaves, which meant tedious tying-up work for someone later.

'Wooah!' There was an impatience in that command now.

Roger leapt down from the binder.

'I would normally try and do this the night before. The first two rounds are always hard work – bloody hard work.'

He grabbed handfuls of cut rye off the canvas cloths and threw them to one side, told his horses to go on and got a further ten yards before he had to jump down again. Slow work, and still a huge perimeter of field waiting to be cut before the job would get any easier.

'They often used to send an old boy round with a scythe to cut the headland before the binder arrived,' said Roger, looking disconsolately at his jammed machine. 'And a bloody good idea it was too.' He dragged more handfuls of rye out of the machine and cut another ten yards.

He was sweating now, and reddening with a rage.

'This is the bit they don't see, this is the hard work. It all looks very nice when it's working, but it's getting it all going. I often say that these old machines are like people – they takes a bit of getting to know.'

Rupert, Courtier and Prince, the three horses, stood motionless, knowing better than to add to the confusion.

As the machine eventually settled into its work the pace quickened, and it was my job to walk alongside and unjam as might be required, and keep an eye out to see that the sheaves were being knotted and not thrown loose onto the field.

Cheryl was in buoyant mood that morning. 'This is real work. This'll make you sweat, lad,' and she grabbed heavy sheaves in her arms and waltzed with them like a girl with a new lover. There was total delight across her face, and indeed who could fail to be infected by this scene – golden sheaves, horses pulling hard, men at work bringing the harvest home? The air was fresh and clear and the tower of Stoke-by-Nayland church seemed as close as if it were in the next field, not three miles away. A good day for work, I thought to myself.

Roger did not do much smiling until he had completed two rounds of the field. This left a wide roadway on to which the binder could eject its sheaves, and the whole operation settled down. There would be an occasional halt to put the twine back on the knotter, or move the levers that set the point at which the knot should come, or some such minor but vital adjustment. But otherwise, the horses marched on and the machine clattered behind.

To complete this Constable landscape of our own creation, the sheaves of rye had to be stood on end to form golden pyramids which are called either 'shocks' or 'stooks', and the operation of standing them up is either 'shocking' or 'stooking', depending on which particular pub you happen to be in when the debate begins. There is even debate about the way they should stand, let alone what they are called when they are upright. Should they be stood with the knot in the twine pointing inwards, or with the knot facing outwards? There are valid reasons for doing it either way, and many a pint of foaming ale has been swilled while the point is debated.

The point of the whole business is to dry and ripen the corn after it has been cut, so sheaves are stood on their ends a dozen at a time in such a way that the breeze can blow easily through them and dry them to a fine crispness ready to be carted away.

'You get hold of one,' said Roger, flinging his arm round a sheaf like a young lad grasping a girl at a barn dance, 'then you gab another. Bang 'em 'ard on the ground and push their old heads together.' For Roger, they stood upright till two more could be hastily grabbed and stood beside them to keep the whole structure stable. When I tried, they just fell. Like threading a needle or chopping wood, it is a knack. If you do not get it at the first attempt, you will certainly not get it on the second. You'll manage it on the third if you are very lucky. Or the fourth.

When two were upright you added to them till you had built yourself a cathedral through which you could look the whole length and peer at the vaulted straw roof you had created. Then you grabbed two new ones and started again. And quickly too, for an extremely jovial and sharp-tongued Cheryl would not be far behind you.

Then I made a serious mistake; I rolled up my sleeves. Even though it was cool for a summer's day, half an hour of humping these sheaves to the vertical brought on a sweat, and button by button cuffs and collars were loosened. The price you pay for cooling air is stinging grazes along every exposed piece of flesh where the cut ends of the stalks rub. Sometimes they bleed a bit, but mostly they itch. They itch the length of your arms and itch in your hair where bits get lodged. Wisps of straw find their way down your shirt till your whole body is a sweaty mass of itch and your fingers are so entangled in the sheaves that to try and scratch anywhere is merely to spread more straw round your body. I thought of those jovial rural postcards of fellows in high-necked smocks heaving sheaves around fields; I had often wondered why they had never stripped sensibly to the waist, like builders. Now I knew.

EIGHT

As the year rolled on, it was becoming clear to me that farming life was an infection of which I would not be able to rid myself. How would I be able to turn my back on this at the year's end? This had been both life enhancing and life changing. How was I ever going to feel I could dismiss it as just another writer's job?

I can't quite remember how I came to buy that horse called Punch. I think I must have been stunned by the news that the chap who had come to see him didn't want to buy him. It wasn't Punch that was the problem, it was his old mate Star who had some trouble with his skin which would keep him for ever out of the show-ring, though he was sound enough for farm-work. As this chap was looking for a pair of show-horses and not just one, he had to say no thanks to Punch. So he became mine. I bought him. Simple as that. I kept this to myself for some while. After all, I still had a pair of ponies at home and no real land to call my own. What would I do with them? Where would I put them? Why was I doing this? Because I felt I had no choice is the honest answer.

Owning a Suffolk horse was a daunting prospect, frightening even.

Not because I hadn't kept horses before; it was simply the thought of being in charge of something so majestic, so powerful, so totally overwhelming as a Suffolk horse that made me shiver for just a second when Cheryl broke the news that I could have him if I wanted. As I had already learnt with my Fell ponies, it is one thing to be in charge of other people's horses where someone else will take the ultimate responsibility; it is another to have only yourself, and the horse, to answer to.

I wandered round to Punch's box to give him a bit of a pat, hoping that this would be the start of a great relationship, but as I patted he merely rolled his eye, showing the whites as horses do when in an uncertain frame of mind. I patted again and he didn't look the slightest bit pleased. It was nearly feeding time and pats were no substitute for grub, not for a horse.

I gave poor old Star a glance as I left the stable. He was a darker coloured horse, stockier in many ways and what Cheryl had called a 'good old-fashioned Suffolk Punch'. He and Punch were an old team; they had been together for years, working in Scotland, carting rubbish, giving rides. I remembered how Punch had bellowed for his mate when we went on that long walk through the bullock field for hay. They'll miss each other, I thought to myself.

I often wondered how I would have felt if farming had been my entire life, and not just part of it: to have been a horseman and to have been forced to work the land in exchange for a meagre living. It is one thing to breeze into it, as I had done, and to use others' lifestlyes as source material. I could turn my back on it at any time if I so wished, and climb into my heated car after a hard day in the field and be certain of a hot bath and a good meal after a mucky day carting mangels with the background comfort of a good income from elsewhere.

Perhaps the thing I would have missed the most if farming had never entered my life would have been the people. Claude, the retired wart-charmer who, incidentally, once listed his professions in a Suffolk Who's Who as 'chimney-sweep and cat castrater' (he used to wrap the cats in a sack and put a Wellington boot over their head; one particular cat, sensing the approach of Claude's knife, made a run for it through the kitchen window and when the owner called for it the next day, he told her it had 'died under the anaesthetic'), always told the story of the man in the village of Boxford who had a lion which he led around on a chain. This man used to ride a 'wall of death' at Clacton with the lion on the handlebars. It sounded very unlikely to me. However, Claude can take you to the spot in the garden of the White Hart in Boxford where the lion reposes. Research later revealed this story to be entirely true.

My farming year came full circle as Roger announced one morning that we were to go to plough. 'I've got your pair going well,' he told me. My pair? 'Punch and Star, they're going real good together,' said Roger. I should have quizzed him further at that point but I let it pass, rather full of myself at the thought of owning a pair of Suffolk horses, oblivious to what a responsibility it was. We collared up; Roger was to plough with Thomas and Rupert, me with Punch and Star. I was just about to walk out to the yard, having watered the horses and checked the harness, when Roger cried 'Woah!' 'Head horseman allus go first,' he told me, and I stood aside to let him pass and humbly followed on behind.

We ploughed till the light started to fade. The church tower at Stoke-by-Nayland had been brilliantly lit all afternoon by the low and mellow winter sun, but that had gone and taken with it all sight of the church. The stillness of the cool afternoon had given way to a gentle breeze that brought a shiver with it, and a mist that hung over the fields and poured down the valleys to smother the village. Soon we would be turning into the furrow for the last time, unhooking the horses and walking them home for a rich and well earned feed of bran, oats and chaff, and all the other grains that these benign monsters devour.

As we walked down the lane, I hoped we might see sparks rise from their feet as their huge steel shoes hit the flints. I had read of it, but longed to see it. There was still so much that I wanted to see, and learn, and do, but I had set myself to work as a farmer's boy for a year and my year was at its end.

I glanced round to see if Roger had finished yet, but I saw that he was still bent over his plough, still calling to his horses. So I turned the plough and with a 'G'up' we marched on yet again, one last furrow.

We threw the earth aside and turned the old soil into new, and as I walked that furrow I thought how nothing could eradicate from my mind the memory of this glorious, fulfilling and inspiring year. I pressed harder on the plough handles, so deep in thought that I almost missed those damned tractor ruts. I thought of the horses, the Suffolk Punches, and how generous they had been to this humble beginner. They could have made a fool of me if they had wished. Surely they sensed that this particular farmer's boy knew less than most. I shall miss them, and the laughter round the kitchen table. I shall miss the good honest labour as well: the drudgery on the wet, cold days on the chilly, sodden soil or in the muddy yard where the only relief from the aching and stinking muck-carting was the prospect of a cup of mid-morning tea passed through the kitchen window. I decided that I must be amongst the luckiest men on earth to have been allowed, for a year, to be part of the magic that happens every day of every farming year at Weylands Farm.

'Wooah ...' I called, and the horses came to a smart halt, just close enough this time to grab a mouthful of juicy twig. I turned them and looked along the furrow I had just cut. It was even darker now, and mistier, but I could see its straightness stretching into the distance. Hadn't Roger told me that a good furrow was one you could see a mouse running along? I called him over for his judgement.

'Roger,' I shouted, but there was no reply. I looked around but the mist had thickened and I could see no sign of him and in the rising whistle of the wind my voice must have been lost. So I stood, for the last time, with my horses and my plough and took one lingering look at my final furrow, till the mist took it from me.

And now I was presented with a major problem. I had somewhat secretly become the owner of a pair of Suffolk Punches, Punch and Star. They were my take-away souvenirs, if you like. I had already bravely hinted to Libby that it would be nice to have a Suffolk horse, and I believe she had become equally intoxicated by the idea, and I was grateful for that. But the existence of Star remained my little surprise. It was resolved one night in bed when she asked, 'When is the Suffolk Punch arriving?' to which I replied, 'the Suffolks are both coming next week.'

And to her eternal credit she never batted an eyelid.

So what do you do with a pair of carthorses that are now yours and are no longer living on a distant farm, but within a few feet of your own home? Those two horses were mine now, not for handing back at the end of the day, but my total responsibility. I remember standing and looking at them filled alternately with pride and fear. They stood in their stalls, champing at their bits; as eager for work as their new owner was terrified at the prospect.

By luck, we were able to buy a five acre field just down the lane; the farmer who sold it to us was even luckier for we paid a ridiculously high price. I imagine he still wears that distinctive grin that crosses the face of a farmer when he's got a good deal. I have never needed to assume it, myself, but I have seen it on many others. But money didn't seem important to me, and anyway Libby was always the one holding the financial reins and over this matter, as with so many others, she was letting me have my head believing that accomplishment was always better than regret. How very lucky to have a partner who thought that way.

That field could best be described as a sketch book. This was where I could practice and learn, and become a real horseman not through watching others but by making my own mistakes and learning from them. And there were plenty of mistakes. Horses sense a novice, and Punch in particular could wind me into a frenzy. We might be engaged in some simple task, like harrowing, and making good progress down the field and then all would be well with the world. Then the damned horse would stop dead in his tracks. His mate, Star, would be quite willing to go on but till both decided to move there was no chance of any progress. And so it went on; stop and start till my temper was at its limits. I strode up to Punch, raised my arm and slapped him hard on the belly, as hard as I could, as Roger Clark had taught me. I dare say the resulting slap could have been heard two fields away. Punch merely turned his head towards me as if to say, 'I'm a carthorse, you know. You'll have to try harder than that.' I eventually fathomed the reason for this behaviour, and it was all old

Gerry's fault – that old horseman at Weylands Farm. He was in the habit of stopping his horses halfway across the field and to anyone watching from a distance he appeared to be making an adjustment to horse, harness or machinery. In truth, he was having a quick smoke and a rest. The horse had learnt the pattern, as horses do, and I never really broke him of it.

The destructive October hurricane of 1987 that swept through eastern England did me an enormous favour, and one for which I will be forever grateful. It brought a massive beech tree cascading across the house, crushing rafters and tiles, causing £20,000 worth of damage, and landing only feet from where the children slept – they didn't notice. But a few months after, when the local builder had finally worked his way down a very long list and arrived at us, a lorry turned up laden with new roof tiles. Out stepped the driver, Derek Filby, a man in his late fifties, white haired, fit and wiry. He spoke in a thick Suffolk accent undiluted by outside influence. Later, I was to become familiar with his turns of phrase born of a century before. He spoke of land 'fair mumblin' off the plough,' or the 'liverish' quality of the soil. He glanced at the horses standing in the stalls, grinned, and from that moment onwards I was not alone in my farming adventure.

It had been a couple of decades since Derek had last thrown harness on a horse but he did it swiftly as if he were putting on his own clothes, knowing every strap and buckle. The horses responded to him as he spoke in a way they didn't when it was my turn. They sensed that here was someone who was in charge: the difference between a horseman and a horse owner. Derek had an undoubted power over horses, although on one or two occasions old Punch defeated him with one of his mid field halts.

We grew everything we could imagine on that little field, Derek and I. We made hay and built a little stack, grew potatoes and even tried mangel wurzels; a ruddy, swollen root crop which gives horses winter succulence in their diets. Some flourished, some faded, but the point was to grow the crops using horses, not the eventual outcome which would have sent any farmer into immediate bankruptcy. I learnt much. I had never before seen how weeds could strangle seedlings, or a crop of oats from the previous year might return to haunt you as an entire new crop appeared from nowhere. For such a small patch of land, though, the effort was out of all proportion. More labour went into those five acres than a hundred might have required. I was not only engaged in my first full-on fight with the land, I was sweating my way up a learning curve with a ferocious, near-vertical slope.

So why the hell did we buy a farm? Wasn't this five acre patch trying to tell me that the outcome of a battle with the land is always uncertain, and weighted in favour of nature? It probably happened because of a growing inevitability. I was caught up in some kind of fateful gale of wind which was carrying me along.

The old farm buildings in which the horses lived next to our house, were not ours. The owners mumbled about conversion into cottages. I have always had a tendency towards ambition beyond my reach and had somehow convinced myself that everything would be easier if I had more land. Slowly, but surely, a change was taking place and what I had thought was already one of life's huge adventures was, in reality, only just beginning.

A word about money: farms do not come cheap. At the time, which was now the late eighties, we were living through one of those booms which everyone believed could never turn to bust. I did less broadcasting as broadcasting tired of me, but even the little I did was becoming better and better paid. Then someone would come along with a sack full of money in return for which I would be required to make a modest effort to appear in their corporate video – usually – ridiculous, high budget, low content, shallow thought out production with a budget the size of a small Hollywood movie. As in all booms, I thought it would never come to an end and as the ink dried on the conveyance for our hugely expensive farm, so too did my flow of easy money dry up.

But Libby was the one who kept this whole project on the wheels and encouraged me down the fateful furrow. When the man who lent us the money asked for a business plan, we remarked that since we were both writers 'the most profitable crop would be the word'. To his credit he accepted that. Boom had turned to bust and the farm lost half its value in the first few years. If he'd ever wanted his money back we would have been flat broke. As it was, Libby wore her finger ends to stumps, writing on a new device called a word processor – Amstrad, actually. That kept us all going. While I cast more seed to the wind, and money with it, she was trudging her own, tough furrow, keeping my dream alive. I'm not certain what the children thought. I think they assumed that all Dads went off and had farms with horses. Children adapt.

Of course, the finding of the farm itself was no simple matter. We had special requirements which were not easy to meet. It needed a proper range of traditional buildings if my dream of recreating a Victorian working farm was to be realised, and such buildings are not easy to come by. It needed to be big enough to farm properly, but no too large to be cripplingly expensive. I suppose I should have given some thought to the quality of the soil but it seemed to be one thing too many to fret about. It needed a nice house, if possible, and it needed to feel right. What exactly that feeling might be is difficult to describe but I wanted something that everyone would recognise as a farm with hedges and gates, where cattle stood at water troughs, and sheep grazed luscious meadows, tall trees providing deep shade from summer sun. I wanted a picture book farm. And I got it, but not until we'd been through a few horror shows to find it.

We toured the length and breadth of Suffolk, not wanting to be far from where the children were happily at school, but all the time realising that may be this was a wish too far. We viewed a derelict turkey farm in a spot that had a remoteness about it that only east Anglia can manufacture. It had its good points but the house was so squat that I could not stand upright in it, and the atmosphere was not helped by the divorcing vendors whose hostility was cold to the touch. Then we saw a lovely farm with water meadows and splendid buildings, but which smelt so strongly of cats that we were forced to decline the offered cup of tea. We learnt from the eventual, and braver, purchasers, that the floorboards were so sodden in cat urine that they had to be replaced, and all the plaster on the walls to a height of two feet. I bet it still stinks.

Some farms were too large, others dreary, none were right. And then a house came up for sale, a fine farmhouse not far way. We drove past. Nice, we thought, and there were buildings. But was there any land? 'There might be,' was the vendor's cautious reply, anxious to conceal the fact that the land adjacent to the house was their family-owned farm of nearly a thousand acres that was falling financially apart. We did a deal. We got the house, the buildings and thirty six blissful acres complete with, as I had wished, small fields and meadows together with a landscape that had a bit of a roll to give it character. It was the prefect place to try and turn back the clock. We asked Derek to come round and have a look. He said nothing at first. 'When do we start, then?' he eventually asked.

It was start of the last decade of the twentieth century and this was where I set about turning that little farm, Vale Farm, into something out of the last decade of the nineteenth. It was March, and it was when I began my diary which was to tell the whole story from beginning to end; it would tell the truth, the whole truth and nothing but the truth about my farming career – the greatest rural roller-coaster ride ever.

NINE

I have not been on my farm very long, just a matter of a few hectic and exhausting weeks, but there is a gradual reawakening taking place, and it is nothing to do with the coming spring. I see it on the edge of the old mangers: dusty and dull when we first came, but now licked smooth and shiny by horses' lashing tongues. Carthorses seem to know when work is coming; they will stand idly in their stalls until they hear the rattle of the approaching harness chains, then start to hunt for the final fortifying grain of food. It is the horse's equivalent of one for the road.

Around the fields our cart-tracks are already changing. Tractors leave two deep tyre-ruts behind them with a mound between, but the repeated plod of a heavily shod carthorse wears away the ground down the middle of the track, leaving a shallow gully. Much easier for walking, and better for getting rid of rainwater, too. We shall appreciate it in the winter when muck has to be carted from the farmyard to the fields. Gates and barn doors that creaked with age have responded to regular exercise and groan no more; gutters, freed of thirty years' worth of rotting autumn leaves, now chuckle to themselves when the rain comes. If you think of our farm as a rusty old machine, I feel we have at least given it the first drop of oil.

But something is not quite right, and it has taken me many miles of furrow-walking to realise exactly what it is. We do not have any gulls following the plough. Now, gulls are to newly turned furrows what young girls are to pop groups: they scream. But no gulls follow me: it can't be just the mild weather. The answer lies in the soil. Gulls do not follow the plough out of some desire to live up to a chocolate-box representation of the countryside. They do it for food. They swoop down, squabble and pluck fat, succulent worms whose world has been turned upside down by the plough. If you have no worms, you get no gulls. No worms mean dead soil, so gulls and living soil go together.

Some of our soil is very dead, and you can tell it from the colour. On smaller fields, old pastures where animals grazed and dunged for years, the soil is richer and blacker and as nourishing as Christmas pudding. But where the earth has been beaten into submission by the combined assault of heavy machinery and chemical feeding, it just sits there disabled, waiting to be fed. A lot of modern farmers know that what they are doing to the soil is wrong, and resent having to do it: a neighbour told me that every few years he needs several more horsepower from his tractor to pull the same plough through the same fields. The soil is dying, giving up the struggle. He knows it, but he has to pay the bills: the economics of modern farming do not leave much room for charity.

My present act of charity begins in a field where we are ploughing with a view to planting clover. Clover is a crop whose ability to fix invigorating nitrogen in the soil has made it the darling of the organic farming movement. If you follow a field of clover with a crop of corn, the corn won't need any fertiliser. Or so the theory goes. And there is further value in it: clover becomes sweet hay, best made by the gentle, unhurried movement of horse-drawn farm machinery. Modern haymaking gear grabs it, throws it, and shakes off the leaf where much of the goodness lies. In the gentle caress of our slow and solid pre-war machinery, leaf and stalk make their way to the haystack together. And when the hay is taken, the clover is ploughed under to release its natural fertiliser, rotting and encouraging the precious worms to turn and aerate the soil.

If we have ploughed well and given the seed a good bed in which to lie, we shall have a good crop. But the tallest stack of the finest hay would not be as sweet to me as the thought that next year, the gulls might find our furrows worthy of their attention. We need their seal of approval.

It is still very early in the year and I went out late the other night to the barn to get a bucketful of barley to boil and then feed to the horses. The air was still, the sky clear and every sound for miles around was quite distinct. As I crept through the doors I heard a rustling like that of a rat. But as I moved further the rustle became more urgent and out of the shadows came a winged white creature with wide eyes piercing down at me. He circled once above me, eyeing me with his marbly stare, and flew into the night. We have a barn owl in the barn.

They don't build barns with crooked oak beams any more. A modern barn is clad in dreary asbestos on a rusting iron framework. Nothing much there for a clawed foot to hold on to, or even a nice knot-hole in which to insert an inquisitive beak. When the rotten walls of our barn were replaced last year, we debated whether it was worth preserving a circular hole in the apex of the roof, about the size of a dinner plate. After an old boy, who years ago laboured on this farm, insisted 'you put that there ol' 'ole back in that barn for them ol' owls', we ordered the builder to carve the orifice. It has paid off handsomely.

Of course, to an owl, finding a farm like ours must seem like dropping in on heaven. The owl population was at its greatest in the days when farmers kept their corn in stacks, and hay in ricks; these provided havens for hordes of mice and rats which in turn gave the owl his daily bread. But when the combine-harvester arrived, which processed the grain in the field rather than in the farmyard, the stacks went, the mice became fewer, and the owls dwindled.

I wonder if anyone of influence is ever going to be as wise as the old owl and admit that traditional farming as practised in the first half of this century, for all its financial faults and labouring hardships, was an inherently healthier way of farming the land?

A visiting student, on his return to college, told one of his tutors that we were planting a crop of vetches; or tares, as they are known in these parts. The student was sharply reminded that this was an old-fashioned crop of no further use and so not worth preserving. Is this poor lad receiving a rounded education?

Vetches are green-leaved plants, sweet and luscious to graze. They are equally tasty if made into hay or silage to produce high-protein feed. The roots fix fertilising nitrogen in the soil, and the plant's ability to form a dense mat means that any weeds cheeky enough to rear their heads are smothered at birth. So the vetch is a fertiliser, rich feedstuff and effective weedkiller. Nowadays, all those properties could be supplied by applied chemicals. But if you had the choice, how would you prefer to manage your soil? With the virtue-packed vetch, or the questionable drum of chemical? And would you have the arrogance to declare that such a versatile plant 'was of no further use'? I hope that the misguided lecturer were merely having a bad day; but if form is anything to go by agriculture is not too careful with its precious past.

If you really want to know what that owl and the pussycat got up to, you must come and camp in my farmyard, any day at dusk, and keep as still as you possibly can. The first thing you will hear will be a rustling amongst the newly spread straw in that part of the farmyard where the horses live. Shortly after the rustling has commenced, you may hear the creak of the unbolted stable door which leads into the yard. It will be the black cat. He gently prizes the door open with his paw and then, hairs bristling down the length of his back, crouches down for the first of several kills of the evening.

But the entertainment is far from over. Shortly after that, swooping low over the hedges and the ditches will come our hunting barn-owl. He will pause on a gate-post or a telephone wire and when he has exhausted his usual hunting grounds, circle the farmyard to ensure that all is quiet. If the barn doors facing the yard are open, he will glide inside, perch on the beams, swoop for a tasty mouse amongst the sacks of corn, and then feast for half an hour. Then, with a powerful beat of his gleaming wings, he returns to the nest. If you are very lucky, you will catch sight of the owl and the pussycat working together, as much a team as a hit squad, flushing out rodents and making the farmyard a better place to live. I cannot believe they would ever go to sea, even in a pea-green boat. They are simply too busy.

I know it is silly, but I always felt that mine would not be a 'real' farm until, in my very own stable, a certain scene was re-enacted in the style of *All Creatures Great and Small*. It is the one where the harassed vet calls upon the grumbling, near-bankrupt small farmer. It is usually snowing and the chilly northern welcome goes: 'Eh, bah gum, vet-er-in-ary. Tha's too late to save our Daisy. Where's tha bin?'

This is cue for the vet to sink the entire length of his arm into the rear end of the unfortunate cow. It is a simple and moving scene, which is presumably why they show it nearly every week.

In our case it was a sick carthorse that needed attention. I played the part of the farmer by greeting him with my running grumble, the one about the lack of rain this last few weeks (I threw a radio across the barn last week when they played *Raindrops Keep Falling on my Head*). The vet, a Welshman, was cast in the heroic Herriot mould. No sooner had he looked at the horse, than he demanded a bucket of hot water.

Buckets of hot water have always been the cue for drama. By the time I had filled the bucket, he had removed his jacket and rolled up a shirtsleeve. Without interrupting the flow of his conversation about the prizes for the breed society's annual raffle, he delved into the innermost intricate workings of my Suffolk Punch with the delight of a child attacking a bran tub. He raked around a little and confirmed a case of worms, and not one stain on his starched shirt.

Two days later worms raised their heads again when my organic farming adviser came to call. With the same gravitas of the vet asking for hot water, this time he requested a spade. We marched out to the far field and dug. You do not find out much about soil by just looking at it. You have to get beneath it, to see the way it holds itself together and how it changes the deeper it goes. You have to develop the critical sensibilities of a common earthworm: worms know worthwhile soil when they feel it. They improve the soil as they burrow: they aerate it and break it up allowing surplus water to drain more easily. To have a field full of active worms is to employ a non-stop workforce in subterranean soil improvement. And they're free. But worms, alas, are killed by some agro-chemicals. So it was more in hope than in expectation that we examined each spadeful like men panning for gold. Not many worms were found. My adviser prescribed a good dose of compost, and rolled his sleeves down again. I won't bother to look again. I'll wait for the seagulls to cry out the news.

I read in a farming newspaper, under the headline 'It pays to be kind to livestock', that far better returns are to be had from pigs which are treated kindly. It went on to report that pigs thrive if given space to roam. Well, it may be news to them but it did little to stir Alice, our Large Black sow. She lives the way pigs were intended to live. She and her piglets wander on grass, hoover up the occasional acorn or windfall apple, and generally enjoy life. Alice is now in-pig for the second time, having reared all eleven piglets from her first litter with no veterinary attention of any kind, no needless jabs, no fuss, no ailing. I call that kindness rewarded.

The other day I met an old stockman and told him of this new piece of research. I have never heard a man laugh so loud. The report went on to say that milk yields vary by up to 20 per cent depending on which stockman handles the cattle. He chortled: 'I could 'ave told 'em that too!' If the newspaper ever reports research into the sucking of eggs by grandmothers I promised to tell him.

Meanwhile, he informed me that any sickly sow should be turned on to fresh grass and given a shovelful of coal dust to root in. 'Best tonic, for pigs,' he said. I expect to hear a newly-discovered coal dust theory from research scientists any day now.

I have also been amused to read that some 'serious' farmers have decided that, by using older varieties of wheat, they would need to add less artificial fertiliser and so save money. Farmers long dead were probably laughed at for sticking to those old varieties when the new ones first arrived. Pity they are not with us so that we can apologise. I sense the tide turning, and it is running backwards.

Lest you should think that I am becoming in any way a competent farmer, let me tell you a story that has been brought to mind by the approach of the harvest season. To adapt the old nursery rhyme, it is a song with no sixpence in it, but an enormous pocketful of rye.

One of the very first crops in this first year has been rye. I was encouraged by my library of aged farming tomes from whence cometh all my understanding of traditional farming. Of rye they say, 'a rank growth so succulent ... the earliest food for sheep ...' Of the grain they remark, 'On the Continent it forms the principal article of food of the labouring classes.' It was clear the rye is one of those hardy crops, thrifty in its ways and willing to grow under farming conditions as barren as Blackpool beach. It sounded exactly the copper-bottomed sort of crop a beginner ought to grow.

Except that I didn't want a crop of mature rye: I wanted a field of fresh, sprouting rye shoots on which to graze the stock. Rye is a rapid grower and even by the middle of winter when all other growth has come to a freezing halt, it is safe to graze it lightly with sheep without doing any permanent damage. It is also good for the sheep to have some fresh green feed at a time when it is scarce; and it is even better for the other meadows, for there is no temptation to turn out the flock when the grass ought to be resting.

But what no book warned me about was the staying power of this stuff. Rye clings to the earth like a drunk to a bar at closing time. Sure enough, our crop flourished and by February the sheep were gobbling as much as they could handle. At one stage we brought in an extra hundred sheep just to keep the flourishing rye in check. Within a fortnight, the hundred hungry ewes had grazed it bare till the shoots met the dust. I sent the visiting flock home with thanks. Within a fortnight, and despite crippling low temperatures, the rye was up and fighting again. I rang the shepherd. The hundred ewes returned and poured out of the lorry like a peckish old-folks'-outing drawing up at a Little Chef. One week and it was all gone. The ewes went home.

Three weeks later the rye was back and sprouting even more vigorously in the increasing warmth of the lengthening days. It had survived two massive attacks and desperate measures were called for. To try and rid ourselves of it, for we had no use for the mature crop, we used spring-time harrows, a vicious wide-toothed comb which ran backwards and forwards till every fleck of green had been removed from the landscape. I looked at the field when we had finished, thanked the rye for the valuable service it had provided in feeding the sheep through the winter, and apologised for putting such a brutal end to its life.

Within a week it was back. Like an unwelcome relative waving from the approaching train, the slender green shoots were once again swaying depressingly in the early spring breezes. I called an end to the game and admitted defeat.

We eventually harvested it, but the worst was yet to come. I thought that at least for all my efforts I would now have several tonnes of rye for sale and could look forward to a profit on the whole tormenting exercise. But the few grain dealers we rang did not seem very interested. I told them those Ryvita people must be crying out for it, but they were not swayed. In desperation I screamed, 'But what about the labouring classes on the Continent? Surely they would welcome it?'

I gave up hope, and was considering a bonfire when a pig-farmer said he'd give me sixty quid for the lot. I did some sums and added the costs of producing it, the man-hours in cutting, carting and threshing. Lots of rye, very few sixpences.

It is quite common on this farm for us to indulge in outmoded agricultural practices; but when we are employing techniques described in a book published in 1865 as being 'antique and primitive', there is an uneasy feeling of having stepped further back into time than is quite safe. But I had no alternative. We have a towering stack of sheaves of corn which, once threshed to remove the grains from the straw, will be ready to be sold. My prospective customer, a miller, asked for a mere half-hundredweight of the corn for testing.

There were two ways of fulfilling his request, the first being to set up the threshing machine. But this is not to be taken lightly. This magnificent creature demands time to manoeuvre into position alongside the stack, the best part of a morning to oil and grease her innermost parts, and six or seven men to feed her with sheaves, catch the grain, handle the straw and bag up the chaff. To put all those wheels into motion for a single bag of corn would be like setting up the scenery for Wagner's Ring and then only singing the final chorus. Anyway, the threshing machine has a long and convoluted intestine which takes some filling, and the modest number of sheaves I was contemplating threshing would hardly provide enough flow to get any corn out of the other end.

So I decided that we would flail the corn. We would spread it out on the barn floor and hit it severely with a stick till it was forced to yield its precious grain. But where to find a flail and, more importantly, a man who knew how to use it? A flail, research revealed, is a hinged stick usually of ash or thorn; one part is five feet long and held in the hand, the other part, about three feet long, does the beating. The two are hinged with a thong of untanned leather, or preferably eelskin. Nor is it merely a matter of 'flailing around' which has come to mean wild, haphazard movements. 'Four or five women', I read, 'range themselves in a circle upon their knees and beat in short sharp strokes following one another in rapid succession around the circle.'

I have never been the kind of man who has four or five women always handy. All I had was my friend Dilly. Nor did I have time to hunt eels or cut ash, so we used sticks. Nor does our barn have the dimensions of a cathedral, like the one described by Thomas Hardy with 'a wooden threshing floor flattened by the beating of flails for many generations'. But, nevertheless, as we bent to the ground, barn doors open to allow the breeze to disperse the chaff and cool our brows, time slipped backwards a century and a half.

We hit till our arms ached but the rate at which the grain flowed was pitifully slow. 'How much d'yer want?' asked Dilly after half an hour. 'Four stone,' I replied. 'Are you jokin'?' he replied. 'There's about a cupful on that floor.'

I never believed that upper arm muscles had so much ache in them. I tried flailing standing upright with the corn on the ground; then to ease the pain I knelt and held the sheaf in the other hand so that at least I was encouraged to continue by the sight of bullets of grain hitting the ground. However, hit them too hard and the grain bounced off the sheet and into the dark corners of the barn to be devoured by mice. Every ten minutes we swept the cloth, poured the

74

corn into a sack and put it on the scales. After two hours we reached the two stone mark. Half-way there.

I read that the flail had many local names; it was sometimes a 'stick-and-a-half', a 'drashel' or a 'Joseph-and-Mary'. More to the point I further read that men working in pairs should keep up a strike rate of thirty flails per minute producing twelve bushels of wheat a day. A bushel is about sixty-five pounds, so our achievement of half a hundredweight in less than four hours, was quite respectable.

Four hours of this work was as much as I fancied. It is well to remember that this was usually the work of two men for the entire winter; and when mechanical threshing machines came to rob them of their labour, they would roam in gangs seeking to destroy them.

But on the basis of one afternoon's experience, ours need not fear the lighted match. Nor must we delve too far into farming tradition, for we soon discover that those who lived it were greater men than we. I do not think we shall repeat the flailing experience. As Dilly said as he headed for home, 'Too much slap, and not enough tickle.'

It never pays to go to plough with a heavy heart. The furrow is too narrow to accommodate human regret and remorse; it has its work cut out to find even room for the large feet of the cart-horses. They have their moods too, when ploughing, although I can never detect in the horse's attitude that he has much going through his mind other than thoughts of getting back to his manger.

That is not to underestimate his intelligence, for a good plough-horse is a clever beast. He knows precisely where to walk, when to turn, where to pull, while also sensing the mood of the man steering the plough. Well, I must admit that the ploughing has been grim this year. We have been deluged with rain on a scale I have not witnessed in my short farming career. Arid ditches have become raging torrents, rainwater hangs in puddles in the hoof-prints left by the horses, the sheep are turning meadows into quagmires.

After the long drought the rain is welcome. But its effects on the ploughing has been disastrous, for the soil is so wet that it has ceased to behave like proper soil should, and has taken on the texture of an over-moist Christmas pudding. Consequently, in the same way that a gooey pud sticks to the spoon, the earth is clinging to the plough as if its life depended on it; and even if it relinquishes its clinch on the breast it will not fall away as a well-behaved slice of soil should. Instead of collapsing neatly against the previous furrow it stands stubbornly upright, heavy, moist and immovable, so that the full weight of a boot against it is necessary to get the curd earth to lie down.

What makes this depressing for the ploughman is the thought that for all his efforts to get horses and plough repeatedly along the field (I walk eleven miles to plough one acre), he might be wasting his time. For the purpose of ploughing is to tuck away last season's soil and bring to the surface fresh earth in which to plant the seeds. This trick only works if the ploughman turns the land completely; if he merely stands it on end, as I seem to be doing, last year's crop will grow again along with a flourish of weeds. Disaster for the organic farmer who has no chemical remedy to check unwanted regrowth. But I am doing my best, and so are the horses in what is turning out to be a strenuous phase of the year.

Old and new technology cannot be mixed. A heavy tractor sprinted along one of our farm tracks recently and left ruts so deep that as soon as they freeze, they will be sure to make a horse stumble. He was doing a job which the horse could easily have done had I found time and made the effort. Now the track is a sorry sight and will stay that way till the spring. By contrast, the field from which we carted mangel-wurzels for three days solid, using horse and cart to remove an estimated twenty tonnes, shows no marks of anything having been across it. Every time I trudge the furrow, I bitterly regret allowing tractors on the land. Their speed and power does not compensate for the scars they leave on this little farm. Every furrow makes me want to pledge never to have one here again. But I doubt I have the strength to resist it. We are not all jolly fellows following the plough.

'Only four furrows to go,' I muttered as I strode across the frozen clods of earth. I paced it out again and, sure enough, four more miserable rounds with the plough and the winter's ploughing would be done. Not that I should grumble. Derek, the old horseman who has found a new lease of life since coming to help on the farm, had gamely volunteered to finish the headland, which is generally reckoned to be the most gruelling of all the ploughing tasks. This is the strip around the edge, about five yards wide, which is left when you have ploughed up and down the field. You go round and round the headland until either you drop, or the horses do, or the job is done.

At one stage I really thought it might be the horses which would not finish the course, for after a mere couple of hours when normally they would hardly have raised a heavy breath let alone a sweat, old Star and Blue were dripping like heavyweights after a title fight. Tough old Derek, needless to say, was untouched by the effort. But although ploughing stiff and cloddy headlands is a fight every inch of the way (remember, this is the land on which the horses have trodden repeatedly when turning at the ends of the furrows) there is a deep satisfaction in providing the frame, as it were, to an artful piece of ploughing. Although to tell the truth this year's ploughing has been indifferent, certainly not the work of an Old Master.

I was checking the ewes and saw what I thought to be an old plastic bag lying in the hedge. Flash, the sheepdog, thought differently. The instant he spotted it he was off with the speed at which he would only move if he thought that at the end of his journey there was something alive. and it was his duty to be in charge of it. He was right; it was a swan. A swan? Ah, go on! There are no swans for miles around. No, it really was. I assumed it to be injured, tired or dying. Fading or not, it was more than a match for Flash at whom it hissed like a pressure cooker. He backed off, so did I. As darkness fell, the swan made its way towards the house and settled down in front of the car, leaving me to decide if it was begging for a lift or euthanasia. I gave it a hunk of bread and went to bed. The next morning it was gone.

Then geese arrived out of nowhere. I honestly had no intention of owning geese, but I seem to have a pair strutting around the farm as if they own the place which they might as well, for if it comes to a territorial dispute I am not going to confront them. At the tender age of three I can just remember being heavily pecked by my great-aunt's gander: geese and I have never got on since. They come at me, heads high, eyes wide, mouths open ready to peck, and hiss and squawk like bagpipers employed by the armies of old to frighten the enemy. I am not going over the top to face them and as soon as they make any moves towards the house I shall surrender and move out. I am told that an attacking goose can be easily repelled with a pitchfork (without hurting the goose in any way) but I am not certain of the precise technique. I think you pin them to a fence and call for help but I am reluctant to try it for there are enough people round here who already think the balance of my mind is disturbed and if I charge around with a pitchfork, screaming, it will only confirm their worst suspicions.

Interestingly, nobody has called to ask for these geese back. It is highly possible that this is the umpteenth farm on which this pair of geese have caused the farmer to live in terror. Their technique is probably to reduce the poor chap to such a quivering heap that he starts imagining swans lying in the front of his car. Having completely disturbed the balance of his mind, they move on. But at least they add to the landscape, keep the orchard grazed, and warn me of visitors. I have arrived at an accommodation whereby they get slung a handful of corn when I feed the hens in return for which they are allowed to hiss at me, but not attack.

I can, however, arrive at no negotiated settlement with my neighbour's Guinea-fowl. These noisy, unattractive, ungainly but cunning birds escaped from next door where they were being fattened for the pot. Sensing sanctuary they headed our way. I do everything in my power to make them unwelcome but they will not go away. I have shooed them, chased them, refused to feed them but they roost every night in the trees overlooking the yard and as soon as I bring out the feed buckets, they swoop to the troughs and steal as much food as the ewes manage to eat. In the summer they are an even greater nuisance for they have a dawn chorus which is always at 3 a.m. irrespective of when the sun rises, and sounds like the rasping of a thousand blunt saws against tough lumps of oak. I have had enough of nights of ruined summer sleep, and sheep robbed from their own troughs.

We have tried to shoot them but with no success. I am no shot, but several chaps round here are and at my request they have turned up with camouflage jackets, Land Rovers and enough guns to end an Embassy siege. So far, they have got a miserable two out of the dozen.

The trouble is, these birds are fiendishly cunning. In the summer, we noticed that they gathered every evening at 5 p.m. round the oat bin. We observed them from Monday through till Thursday and they were as regular in their ways as the chiming of the clock. The guns arrived on Friday at 4:30, ready for the kill. Not one single guinea fowl met its appointment with fate. How did they know? What kind of sense is it that tells them this gut-ful of oats will be their last? Could it be the geese? Are the geese signalling to them? Or is that what they want me to believe, so that I go mad, and abandon the farm to the birds?

You would have thought that I had been farming long enough by now to have learnt not to open my mouth and declare a job to have been a success before it is complete. Of course, some farming jobs never are complete, but merely a staging post in the direction of the next worrying task; we have just sown our mangels but I cannot consider that job complete till they have sprouted and can be hoed. I cannot even congratulate myself then, because I must not tempt fate to blight the crop before harvest. Even when it is carted and stored for the winter, I cannot pop a modest cork lest fate prevent me from a successful ploughing of the land the mangels left behind. And so it goes on, in a relentless sort of way, and explains why farmers are never happy men.

I thought nothing could prevent a decent day's thrashing after the painstaking restoration of our derelict thrashing machine. The men who put Humpty Dumpty back together again did a fantastic job, and as she gathered speed we all nodded at each other, rejoicing at how sweet she sounded as she ran and how the bumps and mechanical knocks were gone, to be replaced by a gentle, well oiled, hum.

I say "we" because thrashing calls for quite a crowd. There are two on the stack with forks, pitching sheaves up to two more who cut the strings and feed the machine. Two more capture the straw that is left behind after the machine has thrashed the corn out of it and build a stack; another is at the end where the corn emerges, and juggles sacks around the flowing spouts like a man trying to keep several spinning plates in the air at once. Some poor soul, usually the youngest, gets the dusty job of bagging the chaff; and another deals with the calder, the broken bits of straw which the machine considers beneath its dignity to handle, and spits out in disgust. I tell you all this, so that you can fully appreciate why what transpired last weekend, before a sizeable audience, represented one of the most deeply depressing episodes in my farming career.

We gathered about nine in the morning, got the thrashing machine running, and after a few irritating halts to shorten drive-belts which had stretched and tighten bolts that were loose, we started to get down to the serious business of feeding sheaves of barley. The thrashing machine has such a complex intestine that it can be several minutes from the first sheaves hitting it to the grains of corn appearing at the other end, and so I did not worry too much when little more than a trickle appeared after the first ten minutes. I proudly strolled around with the oil-can like the chief stoker on the Queen Mary, generally enjoying the rhythmic hum as the machine worked its magic, and after twenty minutes I went to inspect the corn to find that very little was emerging. The flow looked like the drip of a tap when it should have had the full force of the Niagara Falls.

I said nothing and looked again ten minutes later. Still nothing. 'How's it going?' shouted one of the chaps up top. I had to tell him it was coming only slowly but that it would soon be gushing like a newly-drilled oil well. After three quarters of a hour, and still no corn, I called a halt. As the machine ground to a standstill and we all gathered round the empty sack, we noticed the air filled with a distinctive, musty, acidic smell. Mice. Blasted mice! The mice had not only got into the stack, they had eaten every grain of barley and then as a final insult had rubbed my face well and truly in it by behaving as if the stack were a bus-shelter. I thought of the long plodding hours with the horses, preparing the land for that crop. Then the drilling, the hoeing, the cutting with the temperamental binder, and the carting of the sheaves under the blazing sun. And all for nothing, because of the mice. Where was that damned cat when I needed him?

Given the state of the farm workshop, it is a wonder I manage to accomplish any task at all. At least two thirds of the time taken over any job is spent shovelling piles of wood, tools, nails, broken things and unmendable things with the fury of a dog trying to unearth a bone. I am forced to admit, and I do so with little pride, that I have the untidiest farmer's workshop in the realm.

I have tried to mend my ways. Every month or so I tidy round, put all the screwdrivers together in one box, spanners in another. But it is only a matter of days before they are heaped as high as piles of crockery on Harrods sale day. Then frustration sets in, for nothing can be found; this leads to anger and the flinging of items in all directions in frenzied searching, which only leads to tears, and more mess. I have had enough. I am so depressed at the thought of the place that I cannot take so much as a step towards it, let alone begin a tidying process.

The trouble is there is nothing tidy about the way a farm works. If, say, a carpenter is required to repair a broken drawer it will be bought to his workshop, carefully laid on his bench, and he will operate like a surgeon. But when a bit of farm machinery requires intensive care – as our aged, horse-drawn kit is prone to do – it is invariably in the middle of a muddy field, or a ditch, or half-way to somewhere, and it's about to rain. Tidiness of the workshop takes a low priority as you grab for hammers, spanners and bolts and sprint back to the field. When the repair is done you are as unlikely to replace your tools neatly as a two-year-old is to wash up its own cutlery. So tools are dropped on the floor till a heap builds in the doorway,which is then kicked aside when the next emergency arises, for which you are even less prepared because vital tools work their way ever deeper down this metallic heap. I have to admit – this will shock you – I have even gone out to buy a new spanner rather than hunt for the one I need. It is that bad.

I suppose I could brave myself and have a throw-out, but I doubt I could point to anything that I do not need. True, there is an old combustion stove in the corner which has never had its chimney attached because one of the glass panels in the door is broken. I suppose that could go; except that I keep the balls of binder twine on top of it because I have this theory that ravenous mice will not be able to scale its shiny enamelled walls, and sisal binder twine is getting difficult to get hold of. There are several little pots and jars of things which, taken together, occupy a lot of space; but one little pot has got harness-blackener which I use when the horses scrape the leather of their collars, another has Stockholm tar for treating lame sheep. I could go through the remaining two hundred jars and tins but you would be shrieking for mercy; I promise you that none of them can be easily discarded. As for tools, there do seem to be rather a lot, considering that I only ever perform three basic operations which are turning, cutting and hitting. Why do I have a hundred tools to do three jobs?

What I need is some kind of plan of containment. There is nothing there that I do not require, so I simply need to organise it in such a way that everything can be found and, more importantly, there is some kind of incentive to put things back when the jobs are finished.

Surprisingly, I have come across no published advice on the matter. There is a vast mountain of information for farmers on every subject, except this one. No little book of tips, no one-day courses at the local agricultural college, no consultants to be hired to solve the problem for you. Safety rules aplenty, but not a word of advice of keeping your workshop in some kind of order.

Then Mr. Baxter sends me a sinister little note. He says. 'I suspect your problem stems from lack of motivation, but even that can be put right. Do you want to try?' A further letter comes from a gentleman who studied for an MBA and now advises other farmers on how to organise their lives. He claims to have been through CTS – Chaos Tool Syndrome which is a mental disorder – and emerged the other side almost a new man. His system of personal training seems quite thorough, although he reports a "point of marginal return" (MBA-speak, this). For the therapy to work, you must first buy an old railway carriage, he tells me, in order to create "new space". You now need to take your courage in your hands. As soon as an emergency requires a new spanner, grit your teeth and dive into the old workshop and find it. Having found it, and used it, return it to a new and defined space in the empty railway carriage. Eventually, the carriage will fill but everything will be in its correct place. He does warn however that it is inevitable that the railway carriage will become cluttered and the danger is that one then ends up with two unusable workshops and not one. He encloses a bill for £560 for his professional management advice. Shall I pay?

An interesting point arose in a letter which bore a Danish postmark and came from an astrophysicist in Copenhagen. Her first question is why have I got this farm in the first place? Is it for a bet? I am afraid these deep questions should not even be addressed, let alone answered.

It is a characteristic of farmers of the old school that they never throw anything away, and it is a habit for which I have every reason to be grateful. If, say, grandfather's old horse-plough had never been salted away at the back of the barn fifty years ago I would not now be able to exhume it and put it back to work. Most of the gear on this farm is closer to the first than the second World War, and if farmers did not habitually lay down their old gear with the dedication of a connoisseur tucking away a pipe of port, there would be very little machinery for our horses to pull.

But it goes further than machinery. I regularly buy a few bags of barley from a local farmer whose smallish farm smacks more of the 1950's than the 90's. In many ways he is a castaway on his own little island, for surrounding his land are vast fields farmed by machinery so huge that the tyres alone are frightening, and all is computer controlled, managed, audited and regulated; there are more microchips than pitchforks on that establishment. But my barley supplier is untouched by it all, and steadfastly perseveres with his personal low-tech economies. For example, the bill for the barley, which he delivers by hand to save postage, comes in a brown, windowed envelope which is not sealed. I write a cheque there and then, and pop it in the same envelope, resisting the temptation to lick it and spoil it forever; he then takes it away. The next month the same envelope returns and we repeat the ritual. This has now been going on for the best part of two years. The envelope shows no signs of flagging.

I wonder if farmers are as besotted with scraps of information as they are with their artefacts, and even their envelopes? I raise the question because last week I found, on a junk stall, a copy of *Thorley's Farmer's Almanac 1934*. It is packed with information which at first glance seems worthy only of the rubbish bin but which farmers clearly used to crave. It is a slim, pocket paperback and contains all the usual phases of the moon, sunrise and sunset times, and how many pecks to the bushel etc. Nothing wrong with that. Thorleys, who give their address as Kings Cross, London, were makers of animal feed. From here they dispatched around the world potions for pigs guaranteeing "health, rest, contentment and rapid fattening" or "Grula! An exhilarating drink for horses." It seems that Kings Cross always was the place to go for stimulants.

I have learnt much from this booklet, and some of it very worrying. For instance, did you know that one pair of rats can produce 1360 offspring in a year, which in turn can add 5,838 to the total rat population, ending up with 253,762 by the end of the third year? Unnerved, I felt in need of a hefty dose of *Thorley's Pig Powder* "for buoyancy and esprit."

Glancing through the diary section, I notice that the original owner of this booklet recorded the sale of a few eggs on the 26th February for seven shillings and ten pence ha'penny; and 13 duck eggs were sat upon, presumably by the duck, from the 23rd of April. After that, nothing. Was it the income tax that got them: 4s 6d in the pound ? Ramsay Macdonald, by the way, was Prime Minister and Mr. W. Elliot Minister of Agriculture: all farmers should know these things, as well as the fact that Boris III was Tsar of Bulgaria.

Then the Almanac seems to lose its relevance, and we are presented with all manner of information which only a farmer who hoards tit-bits of fact like he saves old gearboxes would ever need. For example, under a heading Multum in Parvo, we read "Dogs remain a major problem in Constantinople ..." or further on, "probably the stalest bread in existence is a loaf now on show in Chicago ..." There is also a long description of how to make a water fountain out of a five-gallon oil drum, and an interesting dissertation on why cows eat iron nails. I never knew they did.

I suppose somewhere, somehow, all this knowledge might come in handy one day. But, please, can anyone explain to me why a farmer in 1934, going around his daily tasks of vainly putting ducks on eggs, would need to know who won the Boat Race in 1887? (Cambridge by 3½ lengths). If anyone can suggest a reason, simply pop it in an envelope; a well-used brown one, please.

We were bagging potatoes; Dilly and Derek, farmworkers of the old school with traditional practices part of their genetic makeup, and I, a comparative novice. Derek asked me if I had a better fork for the job than the one we were using. He said that the one we were using was a "beet fork". He knew this to be the case because the fork had a dozen or so prongs, set close together with blunt ends so as not to damage roots as they were forked into storage heaps. But Dilly swore it wasn't a beet-fork; he knew for certain it was it was a "proper tater fork," and ideally suited to the job in hand.

Not venturing to take sides, I timidly agreed to fetch a different fork, which I was assured by Derek was indeed a proper tater fork. But Dilly did not agree, insisting it wasn't a tater fork at all; "it were a st'n fork!" The stone fork, a relic of the days when gangs of women and children were set the futile task of clearing the fields of stones, we designed in such a way that stones of a size deemed to be detrimental to the cultivation of crops would be lifted by it, but small ones no bigger than ambitious pieces of gravel would drop through. Derek still swore it was a tater-fork, Dilly insisted it was for stones. There was a vague possibility it was actually a beet fork but, after eying it for a while and chewing the matter over, it was deemed definitely not to be one of those. Meanwhile, the potatoes were getting no closer to the bags. In the end, peace broke out with all agreeing that the other was wrong and they were right, which is the conclusion all countrymen seem to arrive at whatever the issue.

At half past four one morning I was strolling back from the lambing field and thinking pleasant thoughts. Things are going much better than they were a couple of weeks back. Some of our early lambs were puny things: unborn twins always seemed to be muddled, limbs wrapped around each other in a politically correct but obstetrically lethal embrace that had to be unravelled before they could enter the world. It is not an unpleasant business, unscrambling twin lambs and seeing them safely born; but I'd rather not bother if I had the choice. It always seems to lead to weakly lambs.

But now things are different. Lambs no longer linger within their mothers but burst into the world, greeting life with a clenched fist, punching into the air and screaming, 'Yes! Where's the colostrum? Mine's a pint.' I like lambs like that. Even better are those who do not even waste energy on the expletives but get stuck into the serious business of survival. I spotted a ewe in labour the other morning and kept an eye to make sure she did not falter. Shortly afterwards, a fine lamb slipped into the world. As it was a warm morning I left her to lick it into shape and mother it, and thought I would return in half and hour to help it to its feet and find the nipple. By the time I got back it was washed as white as something out of a soap-powder commercial, had eaten a full breakfast, and with bloated belly and huge smile was prancing around the field with such vigour that it took some time to catch it and tag it. More of those, please.

Many years ago, we lived next to a retired farm-worker who grew larger onions than anyone for miles around. People would travel distances to marvel at them but, as far as I know, he never did impart his secret before taking it to the grave. All he ever said was 'there's nowt special about onions.' But the one thing I did learn, from his wife, was that Will would never plant his onion seed on a waning moon. Always when the moon was growing, and preferably in the first quarter.

As I walked across the field that night, the moon bright enough to cast a shadow, I thought how silly even to suspect that the arrival of the new moon had somehow influenced the flock. Ridiculous. A truly loony idea. I slept on it, and woke with the notion still nagging. I remembered from a casual remark that my neighbour, Farmer White, had started calving his fine herd of pedigree South Devon cattle at the same time as my lambing commenced. He too reported an indifferent start to his calving season. I rang and asked how things were now. He said they had drastically improved, especially in the last fortnight. A remarkable coincidence.

It was swiftly followed by another, and one with a good scientific basis. A report published by Arizona State University confirmed that lunar phases do indeed influence temperatures on earth, Admittedly, not by a lot. The average temperature boost is all of 0.02 degrees Centigrade, which would seem hardly enough to convince an old ewe that someone had turned up the heating and now was the time to release lambs into a warmer world. But if the moon's phases can alter the temperature, it raises the question of what else they might influence. It may also be that beneath the woolly and insensitive exterior of the sheep lurks a creature far more tuned to the cosmos than we are. So far there seems to be evidence – scant, admittedly – that the fuller the moon, the plumper the lambs and calves. And onions.

Farmers possess, in the moon, a powerful ally which they are not fully exploiting, I now believe. In a phone conversation with the sculptor, Michael Black, I mentioned we were lambing. 'Full moon is it?' he said. He went on to explain that French farmers of his acquaintance always reckon to have a steady flow of lambs up to the full moon and for ten days afterwards. After that, it tails off till the moon is full again and the flow of lambs is resumed. In all the books I have read concerning traditional shepherding practices, I have never seen any reference to this, although amongst traditional French farmers, it would still appear to be accepted practice.

I was thinking these lunar thoughts as I lay in my bunk in the shepherd's hut which now stands in the lambing field. From my prone position, the light of the full moon strikes through the small window across my face for only an hour every night; the rest of the time I can enjoy the loom of a lighthouse fifteen miles away as it sweeps its beam across the sky. Very hypnotic. I resolved that in future I would take more careful note of the rate at which lambing was taking place and the phase of the moon. Although I have my suspicions, I have not enough firm evidence.

But I am not alone in my suspicions that the moon is a tool that farmers could make better use of. *Macdonald's Farmers Almanac 1995* has come into my possession. It is published in America and boasts that it "... tells when to plant and harvest by the moon." It is a sort of *Old Moore's Almanac* but compiled from a farmer's point of view and contains all manner of bunkum, from its belief that the star sign of Virgo controls the bowels to its absolute conviction that sauerkraut should only be made when the moon is in Pisces.

However, there is more; and since much of what it has to say about the influence of the moon could easily be put to scientific test, I must assume it would not make such claims if it could not stand by them. For example, fence posts should be stuck in the ground in "the old of the moon or they will heave out." It would appear that if cattle are branded during a new moon, the brand will almost double in size; if branded in an old moon, the brand will shrink. Here is one I shall certainly put to the test: "Lay a plank on the grass in Old of Moon and grass will all die in seven days. Lay a plank on the grass in New Moon and grass underneath will stay green 28 days." I urge you to join me in this vital experiment.

In my sleepless moonlit nights in the shepherd's hut, I ponder all these things to the accompaniment of the bleating of the ewes, the sweep of the lighthouse's beam, the shadows cast by the full moon. And as I scan the other booklets from the same publisher as the *Almanac* I see that I can read the *Gypsy Dream Book*, or *How to Conduct a Candlelit Service* and perhaps the most telling, *How to Turn Junk into Fun and Profit*. Is my growing cynicism due to the fact that the moon is now waning?

TEN

It would have been no proper farm without animals. I loathe the sterility of the modern agricultural set up which allows no departure for the profit-seeking straight and narrow. The farmers I admired took a different approach; they did not put all their eggs in one basket but relied upon one bit of the farm doing well when the rest may be performing poorly. It was this mixed farming model that appealed to me and so livestock there must be.

Stock are vital to any self-sustaining system of farming. By grazing the land, not only do they give us meat and fleece or leather, but they bequeath us a hefty lump of natural fertiliser to enrich more soil, to grow lusher feed for more stock to graze. I shall not be happy till we have a rich, steaming manure heap of our own and we are ploughing it back into the land to make it alive and fertile again.

Alice, the Large Black sow, is doing her best to make my dream come true, but one pig alone cannot be expected to take the entire task on to even her ample shoulders. Alice has been with us since December, the result of my wife asking Father Christmas for something 'expensive, black and sexy'. She got Alice, who is all three:

a sow of the Large Black variety who now lives in our orchard, and from a distance could be mistaken for a cannonball on the move. She too has found the heat too much to bear, and has retired for most of the day to her sty. She only comes out for a stroll in the cool moonlight; then she resembles an obese witch's cat on the prowl. However, she can be forgiven her eccentricities, for she has recently lost her maidenhood to a Large Black boar from Bury St Edmunds, and motherhood is clearly on her mind.

The cows, on the other hand, have nothing on their minds whatsoever. They are young heifers, fresh from their mothers and enjoying the closing days of their girlhood: the bull is booked for mid-June. If cows could giggle, ours could match any silly bunch of schoolgirls you could name. I take them an occasional bucket of oats as a gesture of friendship, and for a while they will play it cool and sophisticated, eye me across the meadow, and with a flash of their devastating eyelashes they will eventually saunter across. A couple of yards from their bucket they falter in their step, a giggle breaks out, up go their tails, their eyes take on a mad stare and in a wild frenzy they gallop away. Then they start again. We tried to move them to another field last week, but it was a waste of time.

The sheep, however, have been no trouble at all. But I suspect that this small flock has tasted rather more of the comforts of home life than most sheep do. As we loaded them into the lorry, their sad owner wished each sheep goodbye and, looking one ewe in the eye, said: 'Yes, I can see your mother in you, and your grandmother as well.' I felt like a kidnapper.

So, we now have a full house of cows, pigs and sheep ready to take whatever the elements may throw at us. I was watching the sky the other day above the hillock behind the house, and gleefully thought I saw a dark, heavy thunder cloud approaching. But it was only Alice, wandering again.

Wild geese are not the only creatures which can lead a man on a hopeless, heartbreaking chase. Since I took on this farm almost every animal has shown equal talent. Animals are not a problem when they are contentedly munching their way across the landscape; the trouble arises when they have to be moved to another part of it and do not want to go. There is often no choice. In our case, the heifers had to be put on to fresh grass or they would starve; the sheep had to be robbed of their sweltering fleece or they would melt. Then there were the chickens.

We were given a bantam hen and chicks, and sternly warned to cull the cockerels as soon as puberty struck: three randy young bantam cocks pursuing a couple of maiden hens are not conducive to a peaceful farmyard. Not having the skill or the inclination to wring a chicken's neck, I built a wire-netting run and put them in it until an executioner could be found. Within minutes an escape plan had been hatched: the boys were under the wire, free and crowing in defiance. I have now decided on a new approach to poultry keeping. I shall fence in the vegetables instead, since they are slower on their feet, and let the chickens have their freedom until fat enough for the pot. Just how I shall strike I do not know, but my new farming motto is: never admit failure, call it a change of policy.

The heifers are a more serious business. They are three young Red Poll cows with a prize-winning pedigree worthy of Debrett, and for financial as well as protocol reasons they deserve royal treatment. Being of an old-fashioned breed, they will make do on meagre rations. However, I decided that simply making do on arid grass was not good enough for them, and that they must go to pastures new.

When they first arrived the cows were wild enough for a western rodeo. An outstretched hand had them galloping away in fright, a muttered word in their silky, red ears made their eyes roll in terror. But not any longer. The girls have succumbed to my charms. I have learnt two things about cows: that they are curious, and that they are anybody's for a bucketful of oats.

Every morning for a week I rattled the bucket, let them get the scent of oats, and stood still. Day one got no response. By day three they were within an inch, by day seven we had made friends. After that I built a pen out of rusty old gates in the corner of the field, backed the lorry in and the girls ambled up the ramp, as happy to be on the road as a load of children on a school outing. No change of policy needed there.

The sheep, however, are a different matter. Our small flock lives on a grazing marsh which is known for its wildlife. I would care to bet, however, that nothing on this isolated wetland is as wild as our flock of young sheep. Despite the conquest of the cows, I am beginning to think that having so much youthful stock is one of the main problems of starting a farm. Every animal is going through its teenage delinquency at a time when the poor fledgling farmer really needs mature, stable, motherly beasts around him.

Anticipating the problem of catching sheep without a dog, last Christmas we bought an orphan lamb. The idea was to raise it on the bottle, make a pet of it until it believed it was human and would come when called. Once the lamb had been returned to a flock, we would only have to go down to the marsh, call its name, and it would come to us with the rest of the flock following in line as sheep do. We called our ewe lamb Shambles. This was prophetic.

Six weeks after she had been liberated, we went down to the marsh and called 'Shambles!' Disturbed birds took flight, but not one sheep's head raised itself from the grazing position. 'Shambles!' I shouted again, loud enough to stir the rabbits this time. Not a flicker. Then we made a fatal mistake: we decided to round up the flock ourselves.

I had with me a broad-chested chap who has Olympic aspirations and could be said to be 'in training', and an elderly marshman, well past retirement. I offered to get behind the flock and edge them forward while the other two steered them in the direction of the gate. When I banged my stick lightly on the ground, the flock fled as if I had fired a starting gun. The athlete advanced with arms and stick outstretched to head them off, a human barrier. The bleating horde jumped, one by one, over his arm. He swore. They were heading for the marshman now. 'I was in the war,' he shouted, readying himself for the battle. 'Gallipoli, I was at.' The enemy charged and advanced victorious towards the horizon, the traitorous Shambles leading the column. 'I'll head 'em off,' the old boy shouted and using his detailed knowledge of the marsh, shot into the bracken like a stormtrooper.

No sooner was he into the undergrowth than the sheep were out the other side, hell bent on inflicting further humiliation on the athlete. They were panting by now, but not half as much as we were. We gave up. In a mere thirty minutes, a small flock of sheep had got the upper hand of their alleged master, a Desert Rat and an Olympic hopeful. Remembering that all problems can be solved by the adoption of a new policy, I have reached a decision: this farm is going to have a sheepdog. I have reached another decision. It will not be a young one.

Pig-moving, on the other hand, is a game of diplomacy. You suggest a direction in which Alice, our Large Black sow, might like to go, and hope she takes the hint. There is no point in prodding with a stick, for she will freeze. The game needs as many people as you can muster, each of whom carries a board: if a pig cannot see a way ahead, it will not go. You use the boards to deflect her progress: if she heads the wrong way, stop her with a board and let her see only in the direction in which you would like her to go. She retains, of course, the option of standing stock still whatever you do with the boards, but let us draw a veil over that.

At pig-moving time, any visitor is in danger of being pressed into service. It was unfortunate for our friend, the art dealer, that he happened to call that afternoon. Italian leather shoes that had only known the gentle caress of a Bond Street pavement now found themselves up to the buckles in sodden pig litter. But pig-shifting brings out the best in people: rather to our surprise, he entered into the spirit of the thing and when the moment came to round up the piglets he slithered and pounced like a professional swineherd. Fingers that only hours before had been stroking gilded frames, grabbed the hind legs of the protesting, wriggling creatures. When he next raises a finger to bid at a Sotheby's auction, few will suspect where it has been.

Alice and family love the orchard. She places her ample rear against the shakiest of the old apple trees and wriggles her behind till the young apples cascade onto her waiting piglets. They have even made themselves a mud-wallow and are as happy as a family on Blackpool beach.

Once upon a time there was a handsome young Prince, but unlike his fairy-tale cousins this one is turning out to be a real pain in the neck. Prince is our youngest cart-horse and although he has been through nursery school and learnt to wear his harness and pull loads, he is now finding that his maturer years mean I am demanding more of him, He does not like it one bit.

It takes time and effort to school a young horse for farm-work especially when you are as short on experience as I am; but I thought we were getting on fine. He has pulled the heavy two-horse ribbed-roller alongside Blue without any quarrel; he has even done half a day's sweaty work on the cultivator earlier this season and, although puffed, seemed to be enjoying his work. He has hauled harrows, drilled corn. But no longer. He will pull any trick in the book to avoid pulling any heavy load if he possibly can. He will rear, then plunge and will attempt the cart horse's ultimate sanction which is to lie down and refuse to budge. This simply will not do. We are fond of our horses here; but they are not pets and so in return for their keep they must work. He is a dear chap with as fine and friendly a face as I have seen on a Suffolk Punch, but we can carry no passengers. I am putting him back into the hands of experts and hope Prince's fairy tale has a happy ending.

Then, the decision having been taken, my wife let out a cry from the kitchen. There was no terror in it, merely surprise. 'It's a frog,' she cried, 'there's a frog in the kitchen!' We have been having the house painted lately and windows and doors have been open at all hours, so the lines of demarcation between in and out have become blurred. This is why we have a vole nesting behind the fridge and bumble bees in the pantry. She scooped up the frog and carried it through for inspection. As she did so, it struck me that perhaps this was some kind of sign; a pointer to the direction I should be taking to solve all my problems with young Prince, which were weighing heavily on my mind at the time.

The reason is because, as any old horseman from round here will tell you, the frog has magical properties which, if skilfully extracted, can give men supreme equine control. If this is all sounding a little far-fetched, let me add to the melodrama by telling you that as I sat staring into the frog's wide eyes, the rays of the full moon were beaming down upon me. Driven by some inexplicable force, I dived towards the shelves containing the aged farming tomes and there, in a superb work of oral history collected by the late George Ewart

Evans was not only confirmation of the frog's potency, but the recipe for extracting it.

After you have caught the frog, kill it and hang it on a blackthorn twig to dry. You then take it down and clean it by putting it in an ant-hill. The ants pick off all the flesh and leave the bones. Take the bones and place them in the water of a fast-running stream by the light of the full moon (we have all the ingredients so far). One bone will appear to float in a different direction to all the others. This is the famed frog's bone. This potent bone then has to be cured in "umpteen different things", so the book evasively says, dried and then placed in the pocket until required for use. It is thought that the potency of the bone lay not so much in the fact that it came from a persecuted frog but rather in the powerful nature of the potions used in the curing. From what I have read and occasionally, guardedly been told by older men, horsemen were liberal users of everything from arsenic to opium if they thought it would give them the edge over the next man when it came to controlling a difficult horse.

I am wondering what to do next. I have the option of nobbling the poor frog and spending several days searching for ant-hills followed by hours in a damp stream, with no guarantee of success.

On the other hand, assuming that with the help of the fairies wishes can sometimes come true, should I now bravely kiss the frog in the hope that if not he, then the wayward cart-horse will turn into a well-behaved and willing Prince? At the moment, it is my dearest wish that Prince and I should live happily ever after.

I was driving down the lane towards the farm and spotted what looked like an isolated flurry of fresh white snow. As I approached it became clear that the snowy mass was on the move and headed in my direction.

It was no meteorological freak; a dozen lambs had decided that they were of sufficient age to leave their mother's side and had elected the lane as an adventure playground. The bottom rail of the yard gate is of exactly the right height for a lamb to wriggle its agile little body under it. They have it down to a fine art and can squirm their way through, hardly touching the wood; lambo-dancing I call it. I was hardly out of the car before they spotted me and fled as fast as a confused lamb can back to its mother's apron-strings. Some just dived for it, others were overcome by shock so brains did not connect with limbs: front legs were trying to sprint while hind feet were anchored to the mud. Never mind, I thought, soon grow out of it and become as pudding-like as their mothers. It is just a phase they are going through: not quite tender little lambs, but not properly grown-up either.

So I take issue with a distinguished professional study at an American university which was examining the sociological significance of adolescence in human beings and came to the conclusion that 'adolescence ... has been a key ingredient in humanity's evolutionary success ... and it exists in no other animal species, not even apes'. I do not know which particular animals the good professor has been studying but if he would like to come and spend a day on this farm he will find it stuffed with animals all of which have turned adolescent behaviour into an art-form.

Take Alice's latest litter. For the first few weeks they were timid and coy. Enter the sty with the feed bucket and they will whimper at your approaching shadow and, for protection, form a piggy little pyramid in the corner. They are, without doubt, childish. Within a couple of months they will be well into their adulthood, spend most of the day asleep except at feeding times, and only take the occasional exercise by pottering around the field rooting for the odd worm. Nothing too strenuous.

But look at them now. They are bursting with life, developing strength they do not know what to do with, and when I open the door to feed them they come at me like the jets surrounding Officer Krupke in *West Side Story*. Their cheeky little snouts are into every crevice in the wall, nuzzling away at the mortar, pulling bricks away for pleasure. To fulfil their adolescent vandalistic ambitions I have even considered buying a second-hand bus-shelter for them to wreck, or a phone box to rip up.

Prince, our youngest cart-horse, is going through his in-between years too. Working cart-horses spend the first two years of their lives slowly growing up. At two they are gently broken to harness and then given no work for a further two years to allow their bone and muscles to develop. At four, they are re-schooled to remind them of the lessons of two years ago, and then put to work. They do not behave like unpredictable colts, but certainly not like a fully grown cart-horse either.

Prince is definitely adolescent. We have recently been using him for some gentle work with the harrows and although he obeys commands, stands still when told and pulls as much as he is able, he has none of the placid dignity of his older workmates. Instead of standing like a rock, he throws his head in a juvenile way to see what is happening all around him. A mere 'G'up' will have him leaping into his collar with enthusiasm while his more plodding partner has learnt to take his time.

And do not try to tell me that heifers do not display adolescent characteristics or I will ask you to spend an hour in the yard with one at that certain time of the month when the virgin young cow seeks a male companion and is unable to find one. In open fields, heifers will ruthlessly destroy hedges, fences and gates if they think there might be a bull on the other side. If they had underwear, they would undoubtedly start throwing it onstage when the bull appeared, like early Tom Jones fans. Cows with calves do not seem to bother so much; they have long since learned where all that lust leads.

However, I have to say that we have the answer to all this youthful behaviour, one any government might envy. Very soon the grass will grow again and the stock will leave the yard for the meadows. I shall put up the electric fences, turn the power to high and let the short, sharp shock curb any adolescent behaviour.

In the field next to where my maiden heifers have grazed undisturbed for some weeks, a herd of young stock appeared. I knew nothing about it till the phone rang just before seven on Sunday morning – 'Mr Heiney, there's a problem with your cows!' I felt like Mr Barrett of Wimpole Street, discovering that my girls had been out on the razzle. The heifers were, as we delicately call it round here, 'in stock' – on heat, in the heat of a steamy June. We herded them back into the field where they should be, reconnected the electric fence, and turned our backs for a moment. This was long enough for them to toss aside the wire, which was pulsating with 5,000 volts, barge through a spiky blackthorn hedge and dive through three strands of barbed wire. Very perplexing. Especially as my keen farmer's eye had by now detected what they had not, that all the animals in the field next door are girls, too. I blame the heat. It is unsettling us all.

Just when I should have had the sense to realise I had enough livestock in my life, a cow appeared. My wife had been talking to a cattle breeder who had sung the praises of one particular breed, and at the very same time as she was telling me this my eye fell upon an advertisement for the self-same breed. It boasted, 'Easy calving, docile, good-natured'. I decided that the British White, reputed to be the oldest breed of cattle in Britain, was now the breed for me. It also has the advantage of being as white as a sheet, with the exception of the ears, nose and teats which are velvety black. I have had, up till now, red cows; but as I am colour-blind I have suffered many heart-stopping moments of glancing across the meadow and finding the cows have disappeared. They turn out to be standing against a green hedge. So the lighthouse effect of a white cow sounded very promising.

This time, I approached my cattle-buying in an uncommercial frame of mind. I was not interested in carcass weights, feed conversion ratios, pedigrees or championships. I wanted a cow that liked me, and I was prepared to pay for it. If it took money to buy me love, so be it.

I viewed a magnificent herd of British White cattle not far away. Drifting through them like a balloonist crossing snowy Alps, I gasped at the glacial might of the bull, Alfred, and made overtures to every cow in turn. 'This one is in calf to the champion …' they would boast, but I was not interested. 'Is it friendly?' I asked. If they were not sure we passed on. Cow after cow failed the affection test, until one, a looming iceberg of an animal called Sage, detached herself from the herd and ambled in our direction. A cow that heads towards me voluntarily is the sort of cow for me. I asked for more details. She was an experienced mother, having given four good calves; yes, she was very friendly – and no, she was not for sale as she was due to calve in October.

I looked her in the eye, even reached out to stroke the sooty blackness of her nose. Sage did not flinch, but bowed her head respectfully and licked my boots. I put my arms around her neck as a final test, and declared her to be the cow for me. I paid a good price to compensate for disrupting the farmer's breeding routine. Money, I thought, had bought me love.

She arrived last week and soon settled with the small herd; only the sheep took some time to adjust, never having seen a white cow before. As she walked towards the flock, they stood transfixed by her radiance, as if a Messiah had come among them. Visitors to the farm stroked her and had their boots licked and I thought my cow-keeping troubles were over.

But last night, with a strong wind blowing, I strolled up to see her. She saw me approach but did not make towards me as she had on our first date. I inched closer and she looked round, plotting an escape route as cows do when cornered. I cooed her name and she swished her tail. I called to her softly and her eyes merely widened. Then she fled; slowly at first but gathering speed as I neared her. 'You faithless cow!' I cried like a sugar-daddy betrayed. 'You two-timer! Do you know how much I paid for you?' My heart was broken. We were back to the bad old days of shouting at cows. Money can't buy you love.

It is time for the lusty old ram to tup his ewes and it is going to be a long drawn-out affair. In an ideal world, he would only have to be in the field for a couple of weeks – the frequency of the ewe's fertility cycle – and within that short time every sheep would come on heat at least once. Providing the old chap had not been keeping late nights and had his strength about him, there is no reason why he should not accomplish his passionate task within fourteen days. But the first time I used him, it took him nearly two months to get round them all. I know that because the first lambs were born the second week in January and the last few in March. That is a lot of cold nights for this shepherd to be out of doors.

I blamed the ram, calling him an idle swine and publicly doubting his masculinity; but now I must apologise, for it may have been the girls who were at fault.

As I now understand it, although ewes come into season naturally, a bit of a kick-start is not a bad idea. Imagine a flock of sheep on a dance-floor and the only chap present a regular old-timer known to one and all. Familiarity has bred contempt, and those ewes could bop around all night without a single romantic thought crossing their woolly heads. But wait! Suppose a newcomer burst on the scene: a big lad fresh from his motor-bike, the musky scent of sweat rising from his tight leathers. You'd have a dance-floor inflamed with such passion that the fire-brigade might have to be called in. And – here is the clever bit – even the old boy in the corner might start to look attractive. This is exactly the effect I need to create.

To achieve it, I was thinking of using a teaser ram. This is a sheep who has all his masculinity about him but has had a vasectomy. The effect is quite simple. He gets the ewes steaming away over a period of a couple of weeks, and then the ram proper is introduced to the flock. By then the ewes are aroused to fever pitch and after a couple of weeks the old ram is presumably stretchered off the field, mission accomplished.

I was discussing this plan with our sheep-shearer but having pressed his nose deep into the fleece of the prospective teaser, he doubted there was enough smell. 'You want one o' them stinking old mountain breeds with a bit o' smell to 'em. These lowland breeds haven't really got it.' This caused me to rethink my plans. The vasectomy is an expensive operation and if the teaser is going to be lacking in the raunchy perfume department then the whole thing could be a waste of time.

Then, as we were shearing the big ram, a casual remark set me thinking. I was admiring the quality of the pure white fleece and mentioned that I might have it spun and knitted into a heavy winter sweater. The clippers went silent. 'I wouldn't if I was you. Smell, you see, when it gets wet. Smells something 'orrid. Really rammy. That's how it smells. Real rammy.'

So that's the solution! Buy a fleece from a rank, stench-stewed old mountain ram; find a knitter with a failing nose and at the first sign of rain, stroll gently into the field of ewes. With luck, the odour would catalyse the situation more potently than any Chanel ever imagined a perfume could. Needless to say, I would make a tactical withdrawal if things got out of hand.

On Saturday a local farmer retired and held an auction of his lifetime's farming possessions. I planned a late breakfast, a quick fling of the swill at the pigs and the rest of the day spent in gentle bidding. The cow decided otherwise.

As I rounded the corner of the barn heading for the pigs, heavy swill buckets in each hand, I glanced across to the cow meadow as I do every morning and counted the stock. There should be three red blobs, the Red Poll cattle, and one radiant white beacon, Sage, the British White cow. But the corner of my eye caught not one white blob but two. The first was Sage, the other no more than a white smudge among the grass. I reassured myself that it could not possibly be her calf, which was not due for three more weeks; but feeling uneasy I strode across the field to inspect what I hoped would turn out to be a stray fertiliser bag that had drifted along on the breeze.

As I got nearer it was clear that this was no rubbish; this was a calf with the merest grasp on life. The cow licked it and nudged it but it did not rise to its feet or open its eyes. It breathed with a rasping gasp. I ran back to the house, mind racing, and tried to ring my network of local advisers. Alas, they were all at the farm sale, except faithful Dilly who said he would miss the first few items to give me a hand.

I lifted the calf, which was heavy despite its pathetic limpness, and summoning all my strength carried it across the meadow towards the farm-yard. Sage followed, anxious and mooing for her new-born son. I carried him half the way but could go no further, and dropped him gently to the ground where Mother gave him a reassuring lick. Then, with an unaccustomed strength of desperation, I heaved him once again into my arms and staggered to the yard where I laid him on the straw in the warm sunshine, and took a good look at him.

He looked a fine specimen, but half dead. I felt his black ears, nose, and white chest; tested his heartbeat which felt surprisingly firm, and watched his rapid breathing which had a chesty edge to it. He needed food, that special first flow of milk that only Mother can provide. But he could neither stand nor suck. We had to milk her.

We haltered her, tied her up and with a bowl from the kitchen Dilly, our old farm worker friend, relived his golden days as a herdsman. She kicked him. He persisted. Show this man a wild buffalo and he would have a pint of milk out of it within the half-hour. Squirt by squirt, kick by kick, the cow gave us a cupful which we poured down the calf. She had no more to give when Dilly left for the auction. 'Bid for the thatching ladder,' I shouted as he left.

I was now on my own with a calf I was determined should not die. I knew it needed colostrum – the very early milk – from its mother, a couple of pints at least. I rang a farming neighbour only to be told that she'd thrown away six pints last week. The calf weakened by the minute.

In desperation I scanned my books and found a recipe to be used in such circumstances – bottled milk, warm water, egg, castor sugar and cod liver oil. I mixed them, dosed the limp little calf, and was rewarded with an opening of the eyes and a slight raising of the head. The vet came and injected him with some protective medicine, and I then let him rest and be licked by his mother and waited for her udder to fill. Dilly got back from the sale, and reported that just as the bidding was getting brisk for the thatching ladder, the auctioneer trod on it and broke it.

Late that night the calf was no weaker. Every pint of warm – though ordinary – milk pushed him a step further along the road to the moment when he could stand up and suck. Meanwhile it was up to me. He lay on straw under the ruddy glow of a heat-lamp, and in the gloom at the other end of the building I could see the ghostly white outline of his mother, checking on me. Her udder, I noticed, was filling. I never anticipated that when I grasped hold of a cow's teats for the first time, so much would depend on it.

I have never milked a cow before and all the written words on the subject make depressing reading for a novice. *The Standard Cyclopaedia of Modern Agriculture (1924)* states, 'No operation on the farm requires more knack and concentration of attention and nervous energy than the art of milking.' Believe me, there was no lack of nervous energy as, with plastic bucket in hand, I leant gingerly forward and grasped Sage's black teat hoping she was sufficiently distracted from my groping by the bucket of rolled oats I had placed before her. I grabbed hold. The teat was warm, silky, pliable. The wise old cow glanced round with a look in her eye that I took to mean,

'Don't start something you can't finish, boy!'

Cows have it in them to thwart any milker if they so wish. They have a let-down mechanism which, if triggered, allows the milk to flow. If they are not minded to switch on, no amount of pulling and tugging will produce the merest drop. So I pulled just to see what happened, and nothing did. I squeezed my thumb and first finger round the top of the teat and yanked it downwards. The agitated cow side-stepped in my direction and I slithered painfully backwards on to the ground. I bundled myself back on to the stool, grasped again, and she kicked. I managed four or five more pulls, but no milk. The closed sign had gone up on the udder.

Then, in what turned out to be an inspired move, I hauled the calf on to its wobbly legs and gently dragged it to where Mother was tethered. You could sense the old cow changing her mind. She became calm, almost dreamy; there was no more kicking, no shifting from one leg to the other. She licked the calf, licked the oats in the manger and then with the next lash of her vast tongue, spread them over the calf's little head. Meanwhile, sensing my luck had changed, I grasped again and nearly cried with joy when I was rewarded with the merest glob of creamy yellow milk in the bottom of the bucket. It was a meagre half teaspoonful and the vet said the calf needed a massive two pints, but it was a start.

This painfully slow extraction went on for three days. In between milkings, I studied the books and improved my technique from the crude grasping and pulling to a more ordered and gentle sequence of finger movements like a clarinet player practising scales. I was told that one should 'cup one's little finger like a duchess, and squeeze like a ...' but annoyingly they could not remember the rest.

I developed the muscular hand-shake of a wrestler after two hours' daily finger movements. But the rewards were great as slowly the thick, globby, creamy colostrums, known as 'beestings', crept up the side of the bucket. I would pause half-way through milking and fill the bottle and feed the calf while the milk was still warm, then back to the udder for another finger-aching session. I read that the last flow of milk, known as the 'stroakings', was the richest.

Slowly the weak calf grew stronger. Each bottleful had the effect of petrol into a spluttering engine. On the second day he was strong enough to raise his head, by day four he could balance but not move from the spot.

Then, on day five, just as I was thinking I might get the mastery of this milking business, I decided the time was right for the calf to assume his natural role. I milked a pint and gave him half from the bottle. Then I hauled him to his feet, took him to his mother, squeezed the teat and squirted milk on to his lips. Then I plugged the teat into his mouth. Nothing happened. He stood like a bewildered child with an oversized gob-stopper. Then, with one joyful movement of his tongue, he sucked and swallowed. There has been no happier moment on this farm. For an entire week we fought for nothing but that little calf's survival and so, happier than I had been for some time, I went back to the house with milking bucket in hand. I made a cup of tea, poured a drop of the precious milk into it, and toasted his continued good health.

But despite Sage's patience with both me and her weakling calf, she could be trouble. In fact, I am having trouble with two women in my life at the moment. One is a romantic sort, with a beguiling appearance whose tenderness touches the hearts of all who see her. People swoon at the mere blink of her downswept eyelashes; men lay down their cloaks for her in puddles. But, as I shall reveal, she is a cold bitch who has cunningly hidden her frosty heart.

The other lady, who has just come into my life, does not have that instant appeal of the first. But she has swept me off my feet. She is solid and reliable, and has a sympathetic look in her eye when I pour out my troubles.

They are a right pair of cows. The first is Sage, our British White; the other is Prudence, the Red Poll. She has a self-inflicted eating disorder and I am not certain what she is trying to achieve; maybe it is a cry for help, given that she is having to adjust from being a highly productive professional dairy cow to becoming a mere mother of two young calves. But, for whatever reason, Prudence refuses under any circumstances to eat a mangel-wurzel, and this is serious. I have tried disguising them with sweet molasses but, like a child who cares for custard but not bananas, she licks away the one and leaves the other. The Red Poll is an old and noble breed from an age when succulent mangels were staple winter fodder, but Prudence will not touch them: it is as if I had discovered a Frenchman who could not bear the taste of red wine, or a member of the Garrick Club who turned up his nose at Spotted Dick. I have tried leaving them whole so that when she is tired of playing football round the manger with them she might be tempted to take a bite. I have even sliced them into soldiers hoping they will not be spotted amid the oats but this cow will not be fooled.

Which brings us to that other cow, Sage, and her romantic torments. It is now nearly four months since her calf was born and we should already be making plans for the next one. Up till now I have done this by the simplest and most effective way, which is to use a bull but, for complicated reasons, I cannot this time. So Sage is booked to get together with a test tube. The whole process is done by professionals from the local artificial insemination centre, but it is up to the farmer to spot the instant the cow comes on heat.

Well, I have been closely observing Sage for two months now and the only time I have seen any passion flicker across her face is when the morning bucket of oats arrives. She shares the yard with a couple of bullocks who might be expected to get a little fresh with her and so give me a clue; but she is an independent sort of cow who might well batter a young bullock with her handbag if he were to try any of that funny business. Hence my phone call to a neighbouring farmer, the contents of which I will now reveal. Some may be shocked by it.

Me: 'I haven't seen her coming on yet.' Him: 'Have yer seen 'er mountin' t'others?' I reply that I have not. He then asks, 'Have yer 'ad a good look at her Volvo?' Not understanding the question, I ask him to repeat it. 'Her Volvo. Have a look at it. When she's got a red Volvo she's a-comin' on.' There is a long pause while I work out that it is her private parts we are discussing and not her taste in motor cars. We quickly discuss slimy discharges, and wish each other goodnight. I hope that publication of this transcript will bring to a close any cruel and out-of-context speculation.

But that does not solve my problem of spotting Sage at her most romantic: had I wanted to spend my days staring at Volvos I would have joined the used-car business and not taken up farming. Perhaps the clue lies in the mangels. Could it be that they have aphrodisiac properties and wise old Prudence, keen to avoid further pestering calves, will not allow one past her lips? Perhaps I should try feeding them to Sage, in large quantities. If mangels prove to be the food of love I shall feed on. The sooner Sage and her Volvo get into top gear, the better.

This new cow of ours, currently called Prudence, may well have to change her name if she is to carry on like this. Prudence is a solid, sensible name. At the moment she is more of a Cleopatra. If I describe the morning scene in the cow-shed, you will understand why.

Since my failed efforts to get this cow to eat mangel-wurzels (I know that once she has tasted their sweetness and crunched the crisp flesh between her teeth, she will be hooked), I have had many calls from owners of cows suggesting I sprinkle them with oats, slice them, even marinade them in treacle. This has now turned what is normally a fairly routine feeding exercise into haute cuisine as I chop and dice the mangles before stirring them deep into the feed-bucket, vainly hoping the cow will not notice. But it is all a waste of time. She has a tongue as precise as a surgeon's scalpel and will lick every last oat from her manger, leaving the sad lumps of mangel untouched.

I thought at first that she might be objecting to eating greens on principle. She may have heard of the vegetarian movement who shun the eating of meat. Why, she might argue, should the meat not shun the eating of vegetables? But that theory was soon disproved when I offered her some stalks of leafy green kale which she devoured with a frenzy. Of course, she can live a perfectly happy and healthy life without ever letting a mangel past her molars, but when I see the other cows getting such joy from grinding the succulent roots twice daily between their teeth, I feel sorry that she is missing out on a treat.

So every morning I tie her to the hay-rack and we go through a little routine. I ought to explain that although I bought her with two calves, it soon became clear that her massive udder was more than capable of feeding three, so last week I bought another calf for her to suckle. This, I admit, flies in the face of nature and Prudence knows it. No sooner does the little stranger latch on to the rubbery teat than foster-mother's back leg gives it a quick cuff behind the ear which sends it flying across the shed. Bravely it comes back for more and I help it by distracting Prudence, who, if she has something else on her mind, will happily let any numbers of calves hang on her udder. And so I tickle her under the chin, and chat.

Then I had an idea. During one of these tactile gossiping sessions I thought I might wait until she opened her jaws for a bite of hay, and quickly slip a slice of mangel into her mouth. I teased her with kale, which I knew she liked. Then I popped in the mangel. The jaws closed and crunched it. She gulped and it was gone. Every morning I stand there feeding her succulent morsels like a slave feeding peeled grapes to Cleopatra. Or, given the state of her udders, Mae West. After two days I tried mixing the mangels with her oats, but within five minutes she had sorted out the contents of the manger, eaten the oats and left the mangels. I shall play the slave-boy for two more days and then she can lump it.

In the remaining few weeks before shearing, sheep are so vulnerable to attack by every other creature that it is a wonder each and every one of them is not on life-support. I have strolled round the meadows twice a day righting inverted and stranded ewes and have tried with all my might not to shout, scold or show any sign of thinking any the less of them for behaving so suicidally. I have gazed fondly on plump lambs nuzzling their mothers' udders; I have viewed them from a distance with a poet's eye as the snowy white flock drifts across the landscape like wisps of cloud. But still my sheep get me in a filthy temper, and something must be done.

This latest wave of disaffection has been brought about by a change in the weather. We have suffered from weeks of chilly easterly winds bringing cool air off the sea. It has hindered the growth of the corn and set back the grass; but it does have the advantage of keeping the flies in their winter quarters. The cows have hardly had to swish a tail this season, neither have the horses. But more importantly the sheep's deadliest enemy, the blow-fly, has not yet started his murderous little visits to our flock.

I do not want to turn you pale with the gruesome details of what blow-flies do to sheep, but in outline the fly lays eggs in the sheep's fleece which hatch into maggots which go immediately in search of lunch, by eating the sheep alive. The most miserable job of the entire farming year is treating a sheep that has been 'struck' but mercifully it is rare because we are vigilant. But even so, a sheep can be fine at noon and struck to the point of immobility by six that evening. It is that swift.

Now, if the sheep had been better designed this would not happen; for the fly likes nothing better in which to lay its eggs than the filthy rear-end of a ewe. (If this is getting a bit disgusting for you, imagine I am David Attenborough in his best hushed, academic voice.) But the rear end of the sheep is only filthy because nature allows an abundance of wool to grow round it. If there were no woolly bottom, there would be no problem. Of course, I can put the sheep through a poisonous and stressful dip but it is hardly economical for a small flock. There are also other chemical treatments, which are expensive. And so I deal with the problem effectively and traditionally, by dagging.

I take a pair of hand-shears (which must be stamped 'Made in Sheffield' or they will not be man enough to cut a piece of string, let alone the matted rumps I have to deal with) and I hack away till every bottom would do justice to a baby powder advert. It is revolting at times, I admit. My wife brought me a cup of tea half-way through one difficult case and as I reached for the chocolate biscuit, it was difficult to detect where my fingers ended and Cadbury's began. She withdrew the plate, markedly. You can see why the sheep and I are not the best of friends at the moment.

We think we have a ghost on the farm, and I am not in the least bit surprised. Bill, our American visiting farm hand, spotted him. He was unmistakeably a farmworker, in greenish, long coat with a flat cap and brown trousers, standing at the edge of the meadow as if ready for work. Bill thought Dilly had turned up; but Dilly has not been here since harvest and will not be back till mangel-lifting so it was not him putting in a surprise visit. When Bill next looked for the figure, he was gone.

But odd visitors are not uncommon here. Drawn by the sight of the horses at plough, they stand in the lane and will look down the furrow as the horse walks towards them, seeing if he steps neatly without scarring the ploughed land with a misplaced hoof. They think their thoughts and shuffle off. Then there are those who simply want to enjoy the chocolate-box images come to life; but you can always tell them. Their eyes are duller than the horseman's.

If we do have a ghost, I suspect it is one of the old boys who carved their initials in the soft red brick of the stable. Some of these inscriptions are works of art. "W.M.S 1882" must have stood for hours with the point of knife, scratching at the wall in order to leave copperplate lettering of which his old schoolmaster would have been proud. "D.L.B. 1909" spent less time on his but managed to dig deeper into the brick so that his initials stand out where others have faded. If it was a ghost that Bill saw, it was likely to have been one of them.

I wonder why he chose that particular day to give us a call? I wonder if it was to catch sight of a hardly experienced horseman being taught a lesson or two by a young horse?

I mentioned earlier how Prince, our youngest cart horse, had entered into a delinquent phase. After a season's gentle work of harrowing and rolling, where he had shown every sign of gradually learning the lessons that would eventually turn him into a first-rate cart-horse, he decided he was going to have no more of it. We hooked him to the mower but he had no intention of pulling it anywhere. He reared, then froze. I barked at him to 'get on' and he plunged forward with a harness-breaking jerk and froze again. Had I persisted he would eventually have broken the clipper, himself, or me.

But cart-horses are no different from tractors in that if they do not go, they are of no use on a farm; our horses are here to work and not be pets, so I had a long talk with Derek, our old local horseman, about what was best to do with young Prince. We decided to give him one more go. We hooked him to a sledge made of sawn telegraph poles beneath a plywood sheet, Derek got on board. 'Now come on ol' hoss. Yew d'nt want t' b' on one o' them day trips to Belgium.' This was a hardly veiled threat: Belgium is the centre of the European trade in horse meat. 'Come on, Get on!' Prince did not co-operate but danced around, shaking his head, not moving one inch forward. Derek stepped off the sledge, got hold of him, and dragged him forward. He was off, stepping purposely forward, tail swishing, head bowed as he leaned into his collar with the effort of pulling. Derek now jumped back on the sledge to increase the load but Prince did not flinch, merely dropped his head and pulled harder.

Since that day, he has not put a foot wrong. After a couple of days of pulling alone, I harnessed him to the plough with our experienced horse, Blue, and filled with new confidence in the young horse gave them the order to go forward. They pulled away with the smoothness of a Bentley when the accelerator is pressed. There was no jerk, no rearing, no display of temperament. It was like switching on a well-oiled machine and, as I followed them down the furrow, I was able to walk behind Prince for the first time without my heart in my mouth.

Since that day he has been at plough for several hours a day and has yet to put a foot wrong. So what was the lesson? Probably that a true horseman never gives up. I must remember to ask Bill if the ghostly figure he saw was laughing like a drain.

Every year in Britain during the lambing season, the number of lambs that die for one reason or another is roughly equivalent to half the population of London. Think about it. It is a massive loss by any standard, and only the most callous of shepherds would not grieve a little over every lamb that fails ever to wag its tail enthusiastically as it takes its first suck. It is lambing time once again on this farm, and moments of great joy alternate with cruel loss on an almost minute-by-minute basis. Although our losses are well within the average, it does not prevent us from torturing ourselves with the thought that if only we had tried a little harder, stiff woolly corpses would now be gambolling lambs.

But the truth is they never would have been. I am now firmly of the view that newborn lambs have either "Life" or "Death" written all over them and any attempt to change the label is largely futile. It does not, of course, prevent us trying. This year we have built a warming box to treat hypothermia, studied techniques for giving life-saving glucose, taken veterinary advice and filled our cupboards with all manner of potions and been shown how to use them; we have even had one lamb with a wonky ankle fitted with an orthopaedic plaster cast. But some lambs are born with a shadow over them, and labour though we might, there seems to be no changing the tragic path on which these sickly little creatures have been set.

But do not get the impression it is all doom and gloom. We have a fine flock of ewes who have given us some cracking lambs this year; some born with so much life in them that they nearly bounce out of their mothers ready to stand on their hind legs and box the ears of any other lamb that gets between them and their mother's teats; they have "Life!" written across them in bright neon. The greatest thrill is to stroll to the yard on a routine inspection and when you least expect to find any new-born lambs, you spot a couple of squidgy white twins, stretching their limbs for the first time, bleating, while a proud mother looks from one to the other in a harrassed way, wondering which to lick into shape first.

There is little doubt in my mind that when it comes to licking life into their lambs, the ewes themselves have to make some cruel choices. It is sometimes the case that of a pair of twins, one is born much weaker than the other; but it is not the weakling that always gets the life-giving lick of its mother's tongue. She seems to know which is worth the effort and no matter what steps you might take to encourage her, she will stick to her guns. Or am I imagining it? I think not.

Then there are the lambs that wander, and never return. Our lambing yard is secured all round with hurdles but it takes only the tiniest gap for a confused little lamb to squeeze through. We lost a lamb last week when it strayed too far from its mother and took a suicidal route under the fence and into a puddle of icy water. In its chilly confusion, it made the fatal decision to lie down, and drowned.

These are the losses that hurt the most: you curse yourself for not having been there, or not plugging the gap, or lingering in the warm kitchen over a cup of tea when you could have been there, saving that lamb. But before you accuse me of neglect, let me promise you such losses are not uncommon. Ask any shepherd; it is what makes them the phlegmactic creatures they are, and nothing a sheep or lamb could do would suprise an old hand at the game. One old shepherd hereabouts, if told about such an accident, would merely mutter 'Yais, they do that, do sheep'. It would be nothing new to him.

But for all the anguish of lambing, there are huge compensations. We have one particular ewe with a joyously kind face, appealing eyes, and a loving nature towards her lambs. She had a fine pair of twins this year. Picture the scene: she was looking straight at me and her lambs were one on each teat, tails revolving with joy as they fattened themselves on the sweet milk. She looked like a winged angel, propellor driven.

And so when you pass a field of lambs this spring, by all means enjoy them, as I do, but spare a thought for the four million that didn't make it, and the shepherds who have to bear the loss.

It is well known that when the cat is away, the mice do play; but the question is, how do the mice know that the cat is not on duty? It cannot be simply that they scan the horizon, for mice are clearly sensible enough to realise that it takes only the most minor of emergences from the hole for the cunning cat to pounce. No, they have some kind of second sense and I urgently need to know how it works so that I can once again be master of my own farm.

Not that it is mice that are the real problem; it is every other living thing on this farm which waits until my back is turned before creating mayhem. It can be sheep, cattle, horses or pigs; it matters not, but the fact is that I, the old tomcat have only to turn my back on the farm for five minutes for the party to begin. Or is it more sinister than a party? *Animal Farm* famously records what happened when the exploited farm animals decided they had had enough; and it is true that I am beginning to feel like the ruler of a troubled little nation who dare not leave his country for fear of overthrow. I am yet another leader who is having to constantly look over his shoulder.

This is no new phenomenon. I remember a cow died for no real reason at all. I had not left the farm for at least thirty days before, and probably did not go anywhere for thirty days after; but the very day I chose to escape was the day the cow turned turtle and pegged out. At the time I thought it was bad luck, but since then the number of occasions on which fate has struck in my absence would convince any statistician that the mice know well in advance the cat's movements, and plan accordingly.

Our poor old pig, and one of our favourites, Phoebe, died a couple of months ago. That was yet another death-bed scene acted out the one night I had to be away. It is very depressing for Robert, the lad who ably looks after the farm while I am absent, and worrying for me: I am now careful to lift the car keys as silently as I can in case their jangling should ring around the farm, like church bells, in celebration of my departure and bring the entire farm stock out of their corners, plotting against me.

This last weekend was the final straw. Before leaving on Saturday morning, I fed the ewes and lambs and turned them out for the day as I have done now for the last fortnight. When the sun shines, the lambs frolic and scamper in a way that the confined yard does not allow; the ewes nibble at grass, or just bask. For two whole weeks they have done this without complaint, until I went away.

My wife discovered the disaster. One ewe had found her way across a narrow bridge spanning a ditch, made of two railway sleepers. I have tried before to get sheep to cross in this way for it is a handy short cut, but the ewes have always stood trembling at the prospect, like a load of schoolgirls asked to tightrope the Cheddar Gorge. But as soon as my back is turned, they are blessed with new courage and sail across into pastures where they should not be. This in itself is no great disaster, but the ewes leave lambs behind and in returning to get them, knock other ewes into the ditch, who lie there bleating for their lambs who join them and get stuck themselves, and on it goes till a crescendo of horrified bleating can be heard miles away. Just to prove I am not paranoid about the way fate handles my absences, the fox choose that very night to carry off a young goose. We had three of them and each one has been taken on a night when I was not there. I cannot see why my sleeping presence would deter a really determined fox, but he inevitably strikes when I am away. So I am sick of animals cocking their snouts at me, and am beginning to wonder where all this testing of my authority is leading.

Late winter turning to early Spring is a difficult time of year for cows. When the wind blows softly from the south they smell Spring in the air, swish their tails, roll their eyes, and thoughts of freedom flit across their minds. It is the same with me; on the first warm day after the long winter I am thinking of sunny, far-off places, or lazy balmy days waiting for the hay to dry in the blazing sun. It makes me impatient to wind the farming clock forward and plant potatoes, sow mangels, harrow meadows. However, I am sensible enough to know full well that there is still plenty of time for the whole farm to be submerged under a foot of snow, so I curb my wild longings.

But cows do not; and though they are well fed and snugly sheltered, their impatience gets the better of them. Even though the daily feed of mangels is deliciously sweet, and the hay recaptures some of the flavours of last summer, they know that on the other side of the gate something is stirring.

I go to great lengths to make sure that their escapological ambitions are well curbed, with the result that on these dying days of winter their frustration boils over and their sense of mischief scales new heights. I feel like a man who has suddenly found himself in charge of the Belles of St. Trinians.

Their equivalent of sliding down the banisters involves charging round the yard kicking and smashing the mangers and turning over the hay-racks. They stand with their front feet in the water trough for no good reason I can think of, then run riot and chase each other in circles till dizziness or hunger takes over.

But for the moment it has come to a halt for the headmistress had returned. You have never seen gals fall into line as they did the moment she reappeared. Since Christmas, Sage, our white cow, has been separated from the rest of the herd and living in a cow-shed while she reared her young bull calf. Mother and son have done well and so I decided it was time for them to rejoin the herd. I led Sage into the yard, and as soon as the cows caught sight of her radiant white bulk, they froze. They remembered. Sage is a cow who stands for no lip from anybody; her word is law in that herd and if any of them dare to put as much as a hoof in the wrong place, she swipes them with her tail as hard as Miss Fritton ever wielded a cane.

But it does mean one thing; there is going to be more fighting in the dinner queue. When it comes to table manners, Sage hardly behaves as one would expect of the principal of a select ladies' college. She barges all aside, butts and shoves, till she has the manger to herself, and then gorges. Is it any wonder our cattle behave as they do with that sort of example to follow? But at least this twice-daily feeding battle is keeping them all distracted. There are many weeks to go, and as the haystack begins to dwindle and the grass has yet to grow, I am reminded of an old farmer who warned me "April is the hungriest month." That is when the real rioting in the dormitory will break out.

Prudence, our Red Poll cow, has calved again and mother and baby bull calf are doing well, thank you. In fact, they are doing rather too well for Prudence, who was bought from a dairy herd where her whole system had been geared to producing copious gallons of milk. But now that she has only one calf of limited appetite to feed, and as I do not wish to be shackled to a twice-daily milking routine, Prudence has got an udder which gets tighter as the days go by until I fear it can contain itself no more and there will be some mighty explosion, like a bomb going off in a clotted cream factory. Not that it is likely to happen, my vet tells me, for cows have a remarkable ability to adjust supply to demand; a talent which our agricultural policy makers have yet to learn.

Providing they are not overfed, the cow will absorb the surplus milk leaving enough for her calf and no more, and then the udder which now looks as tight as the skin on a guardsman's kettle-drum, would go deliciously slack and I would stop fretting. The only snag is that being a mean farmer, I cannot bear to see all that lovely milk go to waste and so I have decided to buy an extra calf and persuade Prudence to foster it. I hope that my greed is not going to be that little calf's downfall.

I chose a lovely red calf that was exactly the same colour as her natural offspring and put them all together in a shed to see what happened. Compassion allowed the resulting circus to run for only five minutes before deciding to call a halt lest someone got hurt. Prudence was born with great character, body and intelligence, but was not blessed with manners. She has no mechanism for letting you know that she has other things to be doing; she has no facility for saying 'well, I must be getting on then ...' Instead, she drops her head, aims it well into the belly of the unwelcome new calf, and tosses it in the air till it lands, winded. And that is just for starters. When the poor little mite tries to head for the udder, as is its natural inclination, if she cannot butt it she will kick it. But the little calf never gives up.

Some would say they should be left to sort it out for themselves and I have been told this can work, but I doubt it in Prudence's case. I have decided to intervene for if the calf can be allowed to suck unhindered for at least a few days, it will develop Prudence's own scent and she will then think of it as her own. I have a book which advises on the fostering of calves and I have tried tying her back legs together so that she cannot kick. This is fine in theory providing the cow will stand long enough to have the rope attached. I found myself flailing around, rope in hand, grabbing anything that passed with the determination of a sailor aloft a windjammer rounding Cape Horn. It will take a special kind of rope-trick to tame our Prudence.

Along with most shepherds, I make a practice of shortening the lambs' tails shortly after they are born. The theory goes that a short tail cannot get soiled and attract the wicked blowflies in the summer; provided enough tail is left to cover the essentials, it is a practice which can only result in healthier sheep. Traditionalist though I am, I do not resort to the aged practice of shortening them with my teeth. It used to be common to assess the suitability of a potential shepherd by first examining his mouth. If he was like an old ewe and broken-toothed, he could not perform this vital task of docking, nor of castration which was carried out in a similar manner so he did not get the job.

Willing though I am to get my teeth into most farm tasks, that one I can do without. I use a little rubber ring instead, and the surplus length of tail usually drops off within a week and seems to cause the lamb little discomfort. However, I have to admit that the lamb does wriggle momentarily when it is first applied and since I provide them with a little sting in the tail, it is only fair that the flock should ensure that I have one too. This they have done.

Or at least one little lamb has.

Like its fellows, it was growing fast, fed by a rich flow of milk from its mother which I in turn sustain by feeding copious quantities of kale, mangels, hay and oats. There comes a stage,when the lambs are about three weeks old, that they are so fit and vital that if they were to form a rugby club, the scrums would be a formidable sight. It is at this age that they are demanding most milk from their mothers and so you suddenly find you have a flock of hooligans on the one hand, and ever-hungry, milked-out, cot-cases on the other. But I don't mind. It means lambing is over, past disasters are forgotten, and there is all to look forward too. Except for this one lamb.

One morning, for no reason I could think of, it could not get to its feet or, to be strictly accurate, it could not get to its hind feet. The front ones worked fine, it simply had to sit upright like a dog, unable to move other than by shuffling, which technique it soon mastered. My first concern was that it should be able to feed for without regular milk it would quickly die. We penned ewe and lamb together and just to be certain it was not short of nourishment, we gave it a hearty feed from a bottle. This we need not have done, for mother and daughter quickly came to some arrangement whereby the ewe stationed herself in such a position that the lamb could just lift its head and, by great good fortune, find a teat dangling there. Not that the ewe was always so obliging, and on occasions the lamb had to grab for what it could get as its mother charged by; but it 1never went without a meal. I discussed it with the vet and since the animal was thriving and in no pain with no obvious broken bones or dislocations, we decided to let it be for another day.

Six days later, it was even fatter, feeding furiously but refusing to rise from its doggy sit, and so we put it in the front seat of the car in a box, fastened the seat-belt round it, and drove it to the vet. It seemed to enjoy the journey, peering out of the window. In a vet's surgery usually brimming with dogs, cats and budgies, it won many hearts; especially my wife's whose sleeve it nibbled beguilingly as it sat waiting to see doctor. It was an Australian vet on duty that day and with that natural antipodean instinct for sheep, she suspected a spinal infection that might respond to a jab.

A miracle ensued. Within a few hours, the lamb was up, prancing, leaping, cavorting to such an extent that I was hardly able to catch it to give it the second necessary jab. It soon joined its mates and headed for the corner of the yard where I have set up a narrow-entranced enclosure into which only the older lambs can get. Here I give them extra solid feed in order, I am afraid to say, that they should fatten that bit more quickly than they otherwise would. Spring is coming and the customers will be wanting something to go with the mint sauce.

As the little lamb found its legs and joined them at the trough, I paused to consider for a moment what a crazy business this farming is. We rejoice at the miracle of the one who could take up his bed and walk, while at the same time making plans for the last supper. Lambs are only allowed short lives; we must make sure they are good ones.

I have survived enough lambing seasons now to expect an occasional disaster and come to terms with it; even so, the heart can still grieve a little. We lost a lamb the other night because the ewe decided to give birth exactly in the spot where a puddle of icy water had formed after a wintry downpour. She could have chosen anywhere in the six acre field, but reckoned that this lethal location was the best. These things no longer come as a surprise, and I try to keep a careful watch to ensure they do not happen often: yet some ewes have an impeccable knack for infanticide. It would require a personal, 24-hour-a-day shepherd to avoid all such accidents. As I write, a limp lamb is by the kitchen stove having strayed from its mother in the night and fallen into another damn puddle. I have taken care to house the newly-lambed ewes in a field with tall hedges to provide good shelter from the bitter winds of the last few days, but this little lamb made straight for the fence, clambered through the hedge, rolled into the ditch and went to sleep in the icy water. It came dangerously close to a cold death. Having given it a stomach-full of invigorating glucose, we are now trying to raise its temperature to a level which will support life. The mercury in the thermometer is only rising slowly but I think it will make it. Having robbed the Grim Reaper of one lamb, I wonder what he is planning next.

Last Monday night I sat down and wrote a letter to the farrier to explain that the next time he called, instead of three horses to shoe there would only be two. I had decided it was time for Star to retire, and rather than be re-shod he would have his shoes removed and his feet trimmed prior to being turned out to grass. It is not a decision I have taken lightly. Towards the end of last year it became clear that age was getting the better of him and he seemed to be enjoying his work less. I dare say he will still do the odd carting job, but his days on the plough are probably over. Anyway, we now have young Prince under firm control and developing into an energetic and willing work-horse, so I have not been foolish enough to get rid of the old banger without first doing a few miles with the new sports car.

The question is, how did Star know that I had taken the decision? Did he stop the postman and go through the letters, or was he in some mysterious way looking over my shoulder as I wrote it? Whatever, he decided that he was not going to go quietly; and like a soap opera actor about to be written out, he put his heart and soul into the performance of a lifetime.

Circumstances were in his favour. For a start, I was away all day, which is usually the cue for some kind of farmyard fun and games to start.

Robert arrived to feed, as usual when I am away, tipped the horses' feed into their mangers and opened the door to the yard so they could amble in and help themselves. Two horses, Blue and Prince, did; but the third did not. Robert looked out and saw Star prostrate on the ground, grunting and heaving with a look of frustration on his face rather than one of imminent demise. He was "cast". Somewhat like sheep, cart-horses are capable of rolling onto their backs only to find they are then unable to regain their feet. The sodden yard is now so full of deep, squashy litter that his heavy rolling had made a deep impression into which he had simply cast himself.

By all accounts, for I must rely on eye-witnesses here, this also made a deep impression on Robert. He did not know what to do. I would not have known either. I might have first tried a few gentle words along the lines of 'get up you big daft sod' and when that failed, panicked.

My wife, who was on the scene by now, decided that this was a job for the fire-brigade, who at least have a track-record of lifting things off other things. She also decided to ring the vet for the poor horse was thought to be in some distress. Our vet is also a man of some experience in the matter of extracting stuck animals. He once told me of being called out on Christmas day to rescue a cow that had waded into a pond and couldn't get out. While his turkey and pudding cooled back home, he set up planks and ladders across the stinking mire so that a rope might be passed around the cow. After hours of effort he was within feet of her, at which point she simply upped and walked out, looking at them all as she went, wondering why the fuss?

Star was making a fuss by now; but it transpires with the benefit of hindsight that his anguish was more at hearing the other horses enjoying their breakfast while he was still confined to bed.

The fire brigade arrived, and started to dig. If they could get his feet below the level of his belly he might be able to right himself, they thought. There was some worry about his temperature and so it was decided to cover him with blankets and put straw under his great muddy head. Star was now well and truly centre-stage with the spotlight on him, and my only wish is to have been there to see him as they wrapped him up like a baby, and to look him in the eye to see how much he was enjoying it, You see, it is not the first time he has had the fire-brigade to rescue him; under a previous owner he absentmindedly walked head-first into a ditch with a cart behind him. By the time the fire-engine arrived to lift him out, he was fast asleep, still between the shafts, six feet down.

Many forkfuls of muck later he took his opportunity, heaved his massive muddy brown frame onto his brawny legs, shook himself and with indecent haste broke into a canter straight for the stable and his manger. It was such a speedy recovery that it was as if he had come straight out of intensive care and run the London Marathon.

Well done old lad. You have stolen the show and are the talk of the county. It will not be long before people will be turning up to see 'that ol' hoss that the fire-brigade dug out.' For his part, he deserves an award, and I look forward to leading him onto the stage to pick up his Oscar. My principal worry now is this: if I stick to my plan and put him out to grass, what will he do for an encore?

I walked from the house to the stable to give the horses their afternoon feed unprepared for the horrific sight that met my eyes.

Star, our oldest and bravest cart-horse, was lying on the ground, legs askew, head still held high by his halter, his neck twisted into an unnatural position. I thought he was dead.

Thankfully he was still breathing, but had closed his eyes through exhaustion; his neck was dripping in sweat, brought on no doubt by the realisation of his predicament which could easily have been terminal. With much hauling on ropes and verbal encouragement, we managed to raise him till he was sitting up like a dog. Then, to prevent him rolling back again – and to save us the effort of having to raise his not-quite-dead weight from horizontal to vertical – we stuck a bale of hay under his neck.

Then I grew suspicious. The instant the strong scent of the hay hit his nostrils, a transformation took place. His eyes opened wide, his neck which had hung limply was suddenly galvanised, and his mouth, which looked as though it would never open again, snatched a mouthful of the hay as if it were the last bite of forage in the world. The vet arrived shortly after the horse had finally regained all his four, feet, and declared Star to be sound in wind and limb.

It was then that unworthy thoughts crossed my mind. You see, we have a new arrival in the stable. A fine young Suffolk gelding, Taffy, recently broken to harness and ready and eager to start work, has joined our little army of cart-horses. Naturally, as a newcomer, he has been getting all the attention, gazed upon admiringly by all who come to the farm. It used to be Star of whom everyone made a fuss. Being the senior horse with a distinguished career including a picturesque history of having pulled a horse-tram in Aberdeen in his youth, his fame has spread far and wide. He occupies the stall nearest the stable door and so is usually the first to be greeted with cries of 'Ooh, is this Star? Ah, what a lovely boy.' But now things are different. 'Where's the new one?' they all ask, 'Ah, Taffy, what a lovely boy you are.'

When I saw Star sprawled across the floor, I thought he might have had some kind of heart attack, colic, or failed leg-joint. I now suspect him of a serious attack of upstaging. I do not think he ever intended that he should end up in such a life-threatening muddle; it was a sort of prank that got out of hand.

He senses Taffy may be undermining his position of authority, I think: new blood forcing old into retirement. What he does not understand, and what I must make some efforts to make clear to him, is that fun though it is to have a young horse, there is more pleasure in working with an old one. Taffy, just four years old and ready for light duties, is a kindly chap, willing and able. He is afraid of very little and lacks nothing other than experience, which he will gather over the next twelve months.

But being adolescent, he can be tiring. All teenage horses are the same. At feeding time, he has only to hear the clank of the buckets and he is pawing the ground with his front feet, threatening that if he is not the first to be fed he will paw the house down. At the end of the day, when he knows it is time to be turned into the yard, unlike the others he will not wait till his chain is unclipped; instead he will prance on the spot in excitement, fling his head till the rattling can be heard in the next village. When he is finally released, he will trot to the yard as if every second were vital. Very wearying.

He will grow out of this very soon and the stable will become a quieter place. But, as I have been saying to Star, how are the kids ever going to learn any manners if Grandad up the other end keeps putting on a show-stopping display of temperament every time he feels he is being ignored?

ELEVEN

Late one evening the telephone rang in our lonely farmhouse. The air was still and the peace had tempted the bats out of the barn earlier than usual. High in a tree, our resident owl was warming up for a night's hooting. At the modern warbling of the telephone I dropped the muck-fork and sprinted from the farmyard to the house. 'Hello,' I gasped. If Hitchcock had been directing the scene that followed, he would have started the murmur of sinister music at this point.

'Mr Heiney? I think I have ...' the elderly voice quavered, 'I think I have found you a horse-drawn binder,' he blurted out, like a man who had been trying hard to keep a deadly secret, and had just failed. 'I can't tell you where it is, but if you like I will take you there.' He paused. 'I have to warn you, it is a bit primitive.' We agreed to meet the following day, and, with a sense of adventure and conspiracy coursing through me, I went to bed.

To explain: it is all very well to try to work a farm using horses, but where do you get the tools? Horses are simple to buy, but horse-drawn ploughs, rakes, mowers and hoes are not so easily come by. Those that have survived are either found rusting, beyond salvation, in the

123

bottom of ditches, or else they have been tarted up and wastefully strewn around car parks. I have sunk to negotiating a bridle off the wall of a tea-shop, but it is hardly a sound basis on which to equip a serious farming venture. So I rely on agents and spies to do the hunting. Every so often one of them will unearth a crock of gold: in this case, a binder.

A binder is a vital piece of equipment. Without it you cannot harvest your corn. It is an intricate and apparently incoherent assembly of wheels, pulleys, cogs and gears and is usually drawn by three horses. It cuts the corn, gathers it together, ties it in bundles and spits them out as sheaves. When the sheaves are stooked, or leaned upright against each other in sixes, you are left with a field out of any heavy Victorian oil painting called Harvest Scene.

My informant, a Mr Sly, is a retired dealer in farm machinery and has an encyclopaedic knowledge of the contents of every barn in coastal Suffolk. He promised, however, that this barn would be special. We sped down isolated winding lanes into what he called 'bow and arrow' country, although we were never more than a few miles from the A12. We drew up outside a rambling, decayed Victorian farmhouse obscured by dense and undisciplined woodland coming almost up to the bedroom windows. Daylight showed through gaps in the roof, and, in the fields around, the hedges stood as high as trees.

We fought our way to the back door and knocked. It opened an inch or two to reveal a stone sink fed by a lead pipe. Then the door opened fully and there stood Mr Palmer, eighty-seven years old and bright of eye. He was wearing a heavy blue overcoat which, in its long life, had been ripped and carefully sewn together again, but with string.

'Do you want to cut with a binder, do you?' he enquired, fixing me with a watery eye. 'You want to go backwards?' I told him I believed that going backwards was the only way forwards. He said he'd think about it. I sensed that he was wondering if I was going senile. I tried to glean from him some enthusiasm for his farming days, but his mind was set on life's pleasures rather than toils. 'Clacton,' he said, 'Grand place, Clacton. I had some good times in Clacton. Do you know Clacton?' We discussed Clacton as quickly as manners allowed, and then I mentioned the binder again. 'It's over there,' he said. I looked where he was pointing, but saw only crumbling barns and the tumbling bricks of the old granary.

'No, over there!' he insisted, and I followed the line of his stick until I spotted a few roof-tiles above the jungle of vegetation. I looked at my native guide. In his hands had appeared a machete, an oilcan and an adjustable spanner, and in his eyes a gleam of triumph.

A chilly breeze sprang up and I sensed many adventures yet to come before I had sight, let alone possession, of the treasure.

Mr Sly bent down and started hacking at the impenetrable brambles. 'Mind where you go,' Mr Palmer urged. 'I think there used to be a pond under there.' More hacking. Mr Sly's machete swung with a determined rhythm. 'Is the farm set aside?' I asked. 'Well,' said Mr Sly after a little thought. 'It is set aside. But of its own accord, if you see what I mean.' We were now in sight of the binder, and Mr Sly put a comforting hand on my shoulder. 'Don't be too worried if it looks like a load of old bedsteads,' he said. 'We'll get it going.' He opened his bag which contained a brown boiler-suit, an oilcan, three spanners and a half-bottle of lemonade.

The warning had been timely. When I finally got full sight of the horse-drawn binder my emotions wavered. I could not decide whether I had unearthed a treasure or stumbled across a scrapheap. It was rusty and filthy, but bone-dry, having been well covered from the rain. The wood was not rotten and, despite the corrosion, when you applied the spanner bits of it did start to revolve.

I warmed to it. Under Mr Sly's expert control, the oilcan was gushing lubricant into a thousand old bearings. In a burst of excitement he extracted a bit of twisted rod from a heap and declared: 'Look, you've even got a spare sheaf-carrier foot-pedal with it.' Joy.

If you have never seen a binder, there is nothing I can say to give a true picture of its complexity. But, in principle, it is drawn forward by three horses through a field of standing corn. A knife slices through the crop and a set of revolving wooden sails throws the cut corn on to a moving canvas platform. It is carried along, and then mysteriously upwards until it falls into the jaws of a 'trusser' and is bundled into a tight parcel. When the machine senses the bundle is large enough, it throws a string around it, ties a knot, and expels it on to the ground as a sheaf of corn. To be able to translate the steady forward plod of a carthorse into such varied and useful mechanical directions is clearly the work of a genius. Indeed, the man who invented the 'knotter' found that his own invention was beyond his comprehension, and killed himself. Watching Mr Sly conducting his symphony of lubrication, I could see how one might easily lose one's grip. After a difficult rebirth, due to the barn roof having dropped a foot since the binder was last used forty years ago, the machine was loaded on to a trailer and brought home.

It is my binder now: last used, according to Mr Palmer, in the year that I was born. I often go and sit on it, and look, and marvel. I don't see the rust; I have in my mind acres of swaying oats and barley, and our Suffolk Punches drawing my binder through the golden crop.

But harvesting with this machine is not simply a fanciful nostalgic exercise. For a start, we shall have long, undamaged straw, which will make comfortable winter beds for stock, or will thatch roofs: the straw that comes out of a combine harvester is smashed and mangled. We shall keep our weeds under control as well. A combine throws out unwanted seeds; putting weed seed back on to the land is the last thing you want if you are not using chemicals.

All these thoughts float pleasingly through my mind as I sit astride the dormant binder. And then a darker one occurs. 'I wonder if it works?'

A few weeks later, with the binder safely home, I strolled into the kitchen the other day and felt the same horror that must have gripped that sailor in *Treasure Island* when he opened the envelope to discover the black spot. Lying on the table, giving no hint of its latent menace, was a gently curving six-inch piece of wire. I hoped it might be the broken end of a wire coat-hanger; but when I saw a label hanging from it my fears were confirmed. I read the shakily written words out loud so that there should be no doubt. It said: *'Binder Trip Spring from Gordon'*.

The wire was a vital component in our binder which we shall use to harvest our oats and barley. I have been putting off the day when I would have to face this tangled mass of cogs, belts, chains, canvasses and flailing lengths of wood. I have been pretending that somehow this apparently incoherent machine would, if left alone in the barn, pull itself together sufficiently to be hauled round the field and picturesquely turn standing corn into sheaves. But the sight of the trip spring, a gift from my old friend Mr Sly, confirmed that the day of confrontation had arrived.

First I rang my benefactor to thank him for his gift, without which a binder is as much use as a jumbo jet without the ignition key. Mr Sly, you may remember, is the retired machinery dealer who unearthed this 40-year-old binder in the first place. But it turned out that the trip spring was even older than the binder. Mr Sly's brother, a Suffolk farmer who liked the security of a good set of spares around him, had recently died and in his desk drawer lay the spring, put away carefully for a rainy day. Only a man in the know would have spotted its true worth. Trying to buy one today would be like hunting for spares for Stephenson's Rocket. I was grateful to have it.

However, the most pressing problem was not the lack of a spring but a lack of coherence in the entire machine. I set a lad to remove the rust and solidified grease of five decades and give it a lick of paint. But who was going to lay his magical hands on this confounded device and bring it back to life? The phone rang. My prayers were answered. It was Farmer Jones from up the hill, inviting me to view his collection of farming antiques.

I spent a happy evening in his barn enjoying old forks and shovels, gas masks and bits of beloved machines long since departed. But when he showed me his father's old car, I knew that Farmer Jones was the man who could wave a recuperative wand over my binder.

The car was a 1932 Austin Ten and the remarkable thing was that it had been modified for the old man, who stood less than five feet tall. The pedals were extended and, presumably, there had once been a cushion on the driving seat. However, the old boy still had problems seeing over the bonnet and kept hitting things with the front bumper. To prevent further collision, he took the bumpers off. If you have no bumpers, he assumed, you can't bump into anything. Simple. The son of such a man, I guessed, must have inherited a streak of ruthless logic, and if anyone needed a literal mind untroubled by tangential thought, it was the hero who was going to fix my binder. My invitation was accepted and Farmer Jones and his friend, Frank, arrived next morning.

We dragged the tangled machine out to face the field of golden corn. When working properly, it cuts the corn and, by passing it over a series of conveyor belts, gathers it in a bundle. It puts a string round it, ties a knot in it and spits it on to the ground. But as I write, the machine has spat its first sheaf in forty years and I must sadly inform you that there is no string round it. A sheaf without a string is like a sausage without a skin – unmanageable. Farmer Jones and Frank are standing like two shocked men at the scene of a nasty accident, trying to work out why.

I summoned a think-tank of local farmers who still have room in their hearts for these machines, and asked for more advice. One suggested emery cloth to get the rust off it, another spun a nut a quarter of a turn, yet another thought the problem might be with the string. I went away to read a book.

It did not help. The paragraph began, 'In tying a knot, the knotter bills, which are driven by the cam gear, make one revolution, winding two strands of twine around them while the ends are held fast in the retainer. As the sheaf is ejected, the loop around the knotter bills is stripped off over the two ends grasped between the bills ...'

On returning from my library, I was surprised to be met by smiling faces. It seemed there was progress. Sure enough, as the machine trundled forward, sheaves of corn with proper strings tied round them duly appeared. I thanked my friends by stuffing a couple of our own pork chops into their hands, and made plans for my harvest. I decided that having only two carthorses, and a binder requiring three, I would pull it with my ancient little Fordson tractor. This turned out to be the best decision of my farming career.

Robert, our part-time farmhand, however, may have made the worst decision of his. He offered to drive the tractor, having been seduced by a romantic photograph in his father's study showing merry Victorian farmhands slicing their binder through golden corn on a balmy summer's day. In anticipation of an idyll he turned down a better offer of driving an ultra-modern combine-harvester with stereo radio and air-conditioning.

Off we went. We made two glorious sheaves and then there was a sickening crack. The main drive chain had dissolved into a hundred pieces. We patiently jigsawed it back together and cautiously tried again. Then it jammed. Time was ticking by, the sun was getting hotter. Tempers grew shorter.

Then the canvas ripped. Without the canvas belt, the corn cannot move through the machine. We leapt into a car and drove five miles to throw ourselves at the feet of a man who might repair it. We were back on the field within the hour. Off we went. Ten yards and the chain shattered: we fixed it. The new canvas slipped: we tightened it. Cogs worked loose and we meshed them back together. And then all seemed to be going well. We did almost the full width of the field – and the knotter jammed. We unjammed it and drove a further ten yards till the chain snapped again.

Then my temper broke. I beat the binder with the biggest stick I could drag from the hedge. I cursed it, swore at it with sufficient venom to make its grease curdle. Robert was thinking wistfully of the air-conditioned cab that could so easily have been his. Still the machine would not go. I decided to give it one more try, and if that failed I would pick up the phone and call a man with a combine harvester and within the day this misery would be over. We pieced the chain together, tensioned the string, revved the tractor. And it worked. The disparate mechanisms sang to the same tune and sheaf after sheaf cascaded like a bubbling mountain stream on to the land. Rejoicing, we broke for tea. When we got back, the chain broke, then the knotter jammed. The only smiles to be seen are on the faces of our carthorses. They know what they have been fortunate enough to miss.

It was shortly after our first harvest that news reached me that old Mr Palmer, whose binder it had been, had died. He was ninety, or perhaps a hundred. No one seems very certain. His face gave no clues, for it had reached the age where time could have no further effect upon it. But it was his sharp and watery eye that sticks in my memory and the way he fixed me with it when I was first taken to his farm. But now he is dead, no longer to suffer the misery of living on a farm he had long since stopped enjoying. His talk, I remembered, was only of faraway places and fondly remembered visits to Clacton as a young man. I tried to tease from him farming memories, but we always came back to Clacton.

The news of his death came from an auctioneer who had been asked, presumably by a solicitor, to dispose of what assets Mr Palmer had. To the best of anyone's knowledge, he had no family. 'It's terrible,' said the man on the phone, 'things are going very fast. Get over there quick.' His concern was for the horse-drawn wagons which he thought might be of use to us on our farm. I was there first thing the next morning.

It is difficult to believe that anyone would rob an old man whose body is not yet cold, but it was clear that much had been stolen. Two fine old Fordson tractors from the 1930s along with vintage tools from his workshop, even the house had been turned over. I wandered round the farm-yard, deep in rainwater and several decades of unswept fallen leaves. Being careful not to bring any of the tottering buildings down on my head, I opened door after door and wandered through a labyrinth of out-houses, stables, byres, feed stores and harness-rooms. Strangely, there was not a lot of atmosphere. I guessed the heart had gone out of this farm many years ago. It had not been farmed for twenty years.

I was examining an old bale of hay, noticing that although it appeared normal on the outside it was of such an age that the inside had turned to powder, when I heard the distant smashing of glass. Picking my way carefully over fallen rafters and tiles, I found my way through what was the stock-yard and was now so overgrown as to be classified as woodland. Just by the old kitchen door was a blazing bonfire and a skip into which were being thrown old bottles and jars, releasing noxious odours of engine oil, camphor, paraffin, cough linctus and fly-killer. I asked what they had found. 'Just this old rubbish,' replied the lad and threw a dozen more jars into the skip. But I knew they were not rubbish. Mr Palmer was old but he had not lost his marbles, and at the time we were hauling the binder from the shed he still remembered the whereabouts of every spare part. His jars and bottles would not have been rubbish to him. On my own farm I, too, have jars, containing black, brown, golden and treacly liquids. Only I know which is harness-blacking to re-shine the collars where the horses have rubbed against their stalls, and which linseed oil to massage the wooden handles of the plough when they become roughened. When lads as yet unborn turn up to clear out my place, will they know that the black filth in a bottle at the back of the barn is Stockholm tar, which I smear on the driving belts of the threshing machine to give them extra grip?

I wandered into the kitchen, and stepped back a century. Here, only two miles from a major trunk road, lived a man who cooked on a coal fire, heated his water in a copper and baked bread in an oven fired by wood. There was no electricity, and the cold water poured out of a lead spout into a stone sink. Paraffin lamps lit the room.

'There was a lot of old paperwork upstairs,' offered the lad. My pulse quickened. 'Old bills, farming magazines, receipts going back to 1920. Quite a collection.' I asked if I might look at them. 'We've just put 'em on the bonfire,' said the lad, proud of the effectiveness of his tidying. I could have cried. So might old Mr Palmer. You see, hidden among the boring old farming papers must have been treasures: his holiday postcards from Clacton. I hope he is there now.

When it comes to interesting visitors, this farm is never short of them; but glamorous ones are fewer and further between. So it came as a bit of a shock to find a shiny red sports car sweep up the drive, come to a crunchy halt on the gravel and a long legged, blond-haired girl step daintily out of it. I was filling my grease gun at the time and wearing trousers wet from a hour examining rain-sodden ewes: they can be quite pungent when the sun gets on them. I asked if she was in the right place for she seemed to be neither the sort of person who was looking for a decent cow and wondered if we had one for sale; nor the usual customer seeking pork chops. No, she assured me, as she flicked her blonde hair to reveal her piercing blue eyes, she was in the right place. She looked around. 'It's marvellous, simply marvellous,' she enthused.

Putting down my grease-gun and cleaning my hands by uninvitingly rubbing them on the backside of my trousers, I offered a hand of welcome. But she was gone. She trotted over to the barn, then into the stable, looked at the filthy yard which, to our shame, we have not mucked-out yet, and declared it all to be 'marvellous, simply marvellous.'

Who was she? Could this be some kind of clever deception by our local authority? Yes, that's what she was! She was an environmental health officer in disguise and, having found an improperly wrapped rump steak she was going to whip off this ridiculous disguise to reveal a grey suit, clip-board and summons. I hovered.

'It's marvellous, simply marvellous,' she uttered like a needle stuck in a groove, 'it will do perfectly.' My heart beat faster. Did she want to buy the place? After an early summer of trial and torment in the hayfield I was more than ready to sell. No, she was from an agency and wanted to use the farm as background for a fashion shoot. The pictures were for a mail-order catalogue. Marks and Spencer, I think.

I agreed, somewhat flattered. And then, looking at her little red sports car which had had more polish in its short life that all our machinery in its entire fifty year life, I promised I would tidy up, put things straight, get everything in order.

'Don't do a thing!' she insisted, 'it's so beautifully run-down and untidy. It's marvellous, simply marvellous.' She sped away. I went back to my grease-gun, and pondered.

I thought it interesting that of all the well-kept and highly groomed farms in East Anglia she should pick on this one which, by comparison, can look distinctly ragged round the edges at times. I find it a constant battle, especially when both crop and weed are flourishing with equal vigour, to maintain any impression of being in control of what is happening in these few acres. Thistles which were missed by the hoe are now peeping their cheeky heads above the corn, vivid yellow flowers of invasive charlock pepper the corn too; the daisy-like mayweed in the oats spoils a perfect vista of ripening, shimmering heads of grain.

But if you do not use weedkillers, this is inevitable and one of the greatest hurdles over which the organic farmer has to leap is the one that reminds him that no matter how hard he tries, his farm is never going to look as smoothly polished as those around him. But do conventional farms need to look as perfectly tailored as they do? I am beginning to doubt it. I can perfectly well see that weeds compete with crops for moisture and sustenance; but is that any reason to be so ruthless in the eradication of each and every one of them? Perhaps farmers have caught a little of the disease that infects the suburban gardener where every insect that lands is an insult, and every misplaced green shoot is a violation of his personal space. I cannot see that the occasional poppy will do harm to anybody's pride, or pocket. Farmers might well say the grain merchant will grumble to find poppy seeds littering his corn. Well let him grumble.

It is time for a little less tidiness. A few more nettles around the barn, a bit of wild campion here and there and buttercups on the meadows would do no harm either. The fashion world has a word for this dishevelled, unkempt look. They call it grunge. Well, I am proud to be a grunge farmer. I also take some comfort from the fact that Marks and Spencer seem to find something in it too. It is a well-known fact in the retailing trade that what Marks do today, the rest do tomorrow. Any farmer wanting to join this latest band-wagon may apply to me for seeds of just about all the weeds in God's creation.

It might sit easier on the lips of a country squire than on those of a would-be traditional farmer but, nevertheless, I can honestly say that you simply cannot get the staff these days. We are not big enough to need full-time help, nor can the farm afford it; we draw our inspiration from the era when the cheapest thing on the farm was the man; now he is the most expensive.

It is not that people do not want to come and work here for the post regularly brings offers; but the knack is taking the letters and reading between the lines. I have had notes from romantics pleading to be allowed "to share your rural idyll and find deep contentment". Why does my wife dissolve into uncontrollable mirth when I read those letters aloud? Some are more forthright and often with a chilling postscript, along the lines, "P.S. My five Alsatian dogs travel everywhere with me but hardly bark at all after midnight."

But by careful sifting of the chaff from the grain we have had some first-class help on the farm over the last couple of years, and often from volunteers. There was Dick who wrote that he "wished to work out of his system any desire to farm." He could not have chosen a better place to exorcise the demon from his soul. Towards the end of his time I set him off with Derek to cart a field of tares and build a stack. The temperature was nudging the nineties and the crop was heavy, itchy and tangled. Derek, the old war-horse, hardly had a sweat on him after several hours of sweltering forking, but Dick was on his knees and by mid-afternoon with Derek still anxious to cart yet one more load, Dick refused and called it a day. Sadly, I have to report we had a postcard from him some weeks later: the address was yet another farm. I hope he finds someone who can help him. I know how destructive these farming urges can be.

But our greatest success has been Bill, our American from Kentucky whose combined love of Thomas Hardy and Bluegrass music earned him the nickname "Tex of the D'Urbervilles." He left last week and we are missing him greatly. Although he was a good stockman and a willing worker, it was his ability not only to display his moods but to allow others to display theirs which made him a joy to work with. There is nothing more tedious than a character who shuffles off to the barn, muttering, leaving you wondering what is wrong with him, or was it something you said? Not so with Bill. The day we built the corn-stack he was a far from happy lad. He cursed the job, held his pitch-fork high in the air and every time his sheaf did not land precisely in the jaws of the machine, he smote the poor elevator crying 'why won't you take them .. why .. why?' Of course, within half an hour we were all laughing merrily about his outburst. A couple of weeks later when sheep had to be counted and ear-tags checked, it was my turn to boil over. Some cursed ewe managed to escape the vetting by diving through a crack in the gate thus rendering all our counting efforts futile. I too smote the ground. We had a good laugh about that.

But Bill's greatest success was with the chickens. Being from Kentucky you might think that the frying of them would be the limit of his poultry-handling technique, but not so. He managed, by careful feeding, to get them to produce eggs in quantities we have never seen before. Now he is gone the hens have gone back to their lazy one-egg-a-fortnight ways and sadly he has taken his secret across the Atlantic with him.

However, it was not until he had left that I came across the evidence of what a saint this lad had been to endure four months on this farm. He had not been living in the house but in the shepherd's hut at the bottom of the garden. This is not second best, for the hut is a cosy little den and cool and fresh on hot summer nights. I last slept in it at lambing-time and had left on the shelf a half bottle of whisky – for stimulating weakly lambs, you understand. When Bill finally left, I went into the hut to check he had left nothing behind and there stood the bottle with no less a drop of whisky in it than when I had left it months before. When I think what I have put him through during his time here, how could he not have been tempted to turn to that seductive bottle for comfort? I take my hat off to Bill. He was a good egg.

There was an old ploughman who lived in these parts who was known to all as 'Spittin' Mayhew'. He was by all accounts a charming fellow, a great ploughman, and – despite his name – not a man of particularly unclean habits.

He won his nickname because of his peculiar way of starting his horses on their trudge down the furrow. Instead of getting hold of the rein and calling 'G'up', or 'Grrr', or some other throaty growl, he would simply spit lightly into the palms of his hands before clutching the wooden handles of his plough. Over the years, his horses got to know that the smack of their master's lips meant work was imminent. No other command had to be given. It must have looked like magic to anyone who did not know him; like starting a car by merely jangling the keys.

Carthorses get to understand all manner of obscure sounds and signals, but horsemen do have to learn a rather odd language. For example, to get horses to go to the right, we in Suffolk make a noise which sounds like steam escaping from a boiler: if it had to be spelt out it would probably look like 'Wheeesh'. If you are turning horses at the end of the furrow and wish them to come round without moving forward, you ask them to 'Uh back' while at the same time persuading them to do a bit of 'Wheeesh'. If the ploughing is hard and you and the horses happen to be panting a little, the whole operation can sound like a vintage steam rally. Mr Mayhew's spitting system was far more efficient.

His name came to my mind this week after a tragic incident. We have managed to sow successfully five acres of vetches, a succulent green plant that can feed sheep, make hay, smother weeds, and fertilise the soil: a handy sort of crop. After the sowing came the rolling, to press the precious seed into the soil. To achieve this I attached a heavy ribbed roller behind a hitch-cart. This is a modern device which enables machinery normally drawn by tractors to be pulled by carthorses, providing it is not too heavy. It has only one drawback. The seat is made of two planks of the hardest of wood, and driving it over a cloddy field is as comfortable as taking a church pew on the Monte Carlo rally. In anticipation of a long and bumpy ride, I took a bite of lunch with me, wrapped loosely in a plastic bag.

If only the wrapping had been more secure, tragedy would have been avoided. Intent on watching the horses and making sure that every square inch of field was rolled, I failed to notice that every clod of earth over which we rode bounced my precious lunch ever closer to the rear of the hitch-cart until, having scaled a particularly nasty lump of clay, the rapid downward descent of the wheel finally propelled my bag of victuals in front of the heavy roller.

I saw it fall and called 'Whoooh,' but it was too late. A fine pork sandwich lay limply in the earth, the stuffing rolled right out of it. My generously thick slices now lay as thin as Parma ham. The apple was well on its way to cider.

As I rolled hungrily on, I bitterly reflected that it would never have happened to Spittin' Mayhew. His great distinction, other than that which gave him his name, was that he was probably the only ploughman regularly to carry a handbag. He had learnt what I am just beginning to discover: that when you set off to a field with a pair of carthorses, the last thing you want to do is return home before the job is finished. After all, the round trip could be several miles. Hence the handbag, which had in it all that a man might need to get him out of any tricky situation that field work could throw up.

I am now drawing up a list of contents for mine. Ideally, I should find out exactly what Mayhew had in his, so I am scouring the memories of those who knew him. One day, when ploughing, someone lost a button off their trousers. 'Now hold yer on a minute', Mayhew said, and produced from his treasures a needle and thread. On another occasion some machinery snapped and out of the famous bag came a brace-and-bit. But it is easy to get carried away. I am tempted to stick by the old horseman's rule that all you could ever need was a shilling, a shut-knife and a piece of string: string to mend the harness, the knife to cut it and a shilling for a pint of ale.

I now raise that pint and toast my farming friends – the best I ever had.

TWELVE

I love the eternal change of the seasons more than anything else, but I cannot make up my mind about winter on farms. It is either a time of wild beauty to be enjoyed, or merely a period of intense drudgery. For rural writers it has always been the former, and they are invariably more eloquent in their descriptions of frosty, ice-bound mornings than they are in depicting sultry summer days. I can understand why. Senses are heightened: details too commonplace to be worth noting on ordinary days are observed and enjoyed when set against a background of intense bleakness.

For example, when it became clear that snow was imminent, I took a horse and cart to cut a few loads of kale so that whatever the weather there would be something fresh for the stock to chew over. The land was hard as rock, and as my billhook struck the earth when slicing through the stems of the kale it made sparks. The horse, with his tail to the bitter wind, dropped a heap of dung which steamed with such ferocity that I swear you could have boiled a kettle on it. On an ordinary working day I might not have noticed.

As we trundled home with the last load, the heaviness in the snow-laden sky became oppressive and I glanced at the sheep. My sheep are cunning and are well aware that they can manipulate their inexperienced master. It seems that it has only to cross my mind that they may need an extra feed for one of them to give a heart-rending, hungry bleat. On this occasion, I thought that our pregnant ewes would be better off in the shelter of the farmyard. The instant the thought occurred, the first flakes of snow fell and a cold, lone sheep ambled towards me with plea written across its face. Snow was being driven horizontally and the wind had an edge to it keener than any blade on a scythe. I set my sheepdog, Flash, to gather the flock and watched as he became a dark smudge moving swiftly through the white blur. Bringing sheep safely home in a blizzard is a memory I shall treasure.

So much for the romance. What about the harsh facts of daily life? Well, I do not feel moved to write in poetic terms about the early mornings when penetrating frosts bite into my cracked fingertips. I cannot begin to describe the gloom when I find snow has blown under the barn roof and covered several hundred pounds' worth of feed: it is no problem now but the feed could be ruined when the thaw comes. I will not describe to you the frustration when numb fingers are trying to undo a chain on a gate, or the feeling when the metal feed scoop freezes to your fingers.

And all this fumbling, shivering and lugging of heavy water buckets is set against a background of cows, sheep, horses and pigs all raising their voices and stamping their feet, demanding food to keep out the bitter cold. There have been times in the last few days when I have stood, frozen, in the middle of the yard and screamed at the lot of them. There was not much poetry in it.

I can honestly say that almost every climatological experience has confronted me. I have farmed through storm and tempest, flood and drought. But I have been cheated of just one thing, for it seems that despite the cold of recent days, my farming career will pass without it having had to survive one single really bitter winter. East Anglia used to be famous for them. Indeed, when we first came to live here a mere thirteen years ago, every winter was punctuated with massive falls of snow which, one year, caused food to be dropped by helicopters to relieve the snow-bound villagers. I remember one night, with the temperature outside falling to minus 16, inside it was too cold to sleep. At three o'clock in the morning we got up, lit the fire and huddled round that. Very *Dr. Zhivago*.

Of course, we have had cold snaps when pipes have frozen and the ice on the troughs has had to be broken with the feed bucket, but they have never lasted for more than a few days. And then it has been back to those mild and muggy days which confuse the snowdrops. And us too. This year, for example, our cart-horses were still on the meadows as late as the first weekend in December. This is unprecedented. In previous years their broad, iron-shod feet have been churning the sodden pastures to mud by early October and they have had to be brought into strawed yards to save the grass from any further damage. Not this year. Following the warm autumn, the meadows were firm and lush enough to be used as a golf course. Traditionally, the first of November was the date on which horses were brought in for the winter, but that was in the days before someone took hold of the seasons and gave them a good shaking up. Oh, for a long, steady slide both into winter and out of it, and not a twitchy sort of weather that goes from baking to snow-bound within twenty-four hours.

Not that I terribly enjoy winter mornings, I just feel that they are something which we ought to go through both for our physical and mental health. Cutting into a haystack, grabbing hold of the icy handle of the stack-knife, feeling the chill of the shaft of the pitch-fork, is no great treat at the time; but somehow the memory of it carries over into the following season's haymaking and makes it all the more worthwhile and therefore enjoyable. One remembers the hunger on the faces of the livestock and the satisfaction of feeding them. It is the same sensation as having bottled home-made jam in the summer and then spending the winter months piling it on to hot toast. Would the making of it have the same thrill if you knew that the winter was probably going to be so mild that you only fancied salad?

I am not the only one to think this way. It has been reported recently that Russia is suffering an early and severe winter, and that some, at least, of the Russians are delighted. One Russian who moved to warmer climes is reported to have wept in longing for a harsh winter again. "Minus 40 is when I come alive, the air is so pure and refreshing." I agree; bitter winter weather is invigorating. It allows new sensitivities to flourish, and a whole new perception of the land to be enjoyed. The writer John Stewart Collis crystallised for me the reasons why a hard winter does the spirit no harm. Of his days on the land he wrote:

"... is there any silence so deep and rare as that bestowed by snow? ... it is a wonderful thing in our machine age to find the world in the morning ankle-deep in snow. The unwonted silence that falls upon our life is truly magnificent. One heavy fall of snow in the country, and modern civilisation is silenced!"

That's the point. Life in both town and country has become insulated from the direct influence of the force of nature, and when nature loses her temper and slaps us across the face with a blast of freezing fog on the M25, it puts us suitably in our place. On farms too, where the advance of agricultural science is such that for the first time in history the battle between man and nature is tipping in favour of the farmer, it does us no harm to be reminded that all it takes is for nature to dump six inches of snow on us for "modern civilisation to be silenced."

Winter is good for us, and the more bitter the better. Put another log on the fire, and pass the vodka, comrade.

Although geologists may think differently, there are only two types of soil in Britain. There is "boy's land," and there is the other sort – which is never actually referred to as "man's land" but that is what they mean. Boy's land is the easy stuff to handle; it is usually sandy and light, free-draining and quick to dry after heavy rain. It may not be as fertile as some soils, but it can be easily worked. It is so forgiving that it can be worked by an ignorant boy.

The other type of soil is not so yielding or cooperative. We have plenty of this heavy, clay land hereabouts and over the centuries it has reduced farmers to tears. It has either made men of them, or left them broken and ruined. Learning to farm this heavy land is the hardest of schools, but the rewards are great, for there is huge fertility locked within it. When wet, it is unworkable. It sits like molten brick, ready to swallow any tractor wheel or horse's hoof that dares to cross it. It will absorb the winter rains to such a depth that even a week's dry weather in the spring will conceal a soggy mass of soil beneath the surface. But when the dry weather does eventually arrive and the land starts to dry out your problems are far from over, for it will then bake itself into impenetrable clods that will only yield to the mightiest machinery. 'Steely' is how our old horseman, Derek, describes it. It is the sort of soil which is either sticking to your boots, daring to take one pace more; or when dry, making a stroll across the field as uncomfortable as a walk through brick rubble on a building site.

But somewhere between these two states, there comes a time when the land is fit to work. The secret of success lies in knowing when that time has come. I thought my time was right last week, but I was not certain.

I mentioned this to Mr. Sheldrick, a distinguished ironmonger in our local market town who usefully stocks spares for oil-lamps and until recently was a reliable source of rings for pigs' noses. Now he is a fund of tales from his Cambridgeshire boyhood. He remembered the story of the boy who, early one spring, was driving a tractor across a field attempting to make a seedbed. He was not getting very far. It was heavy land, certainly not boy's land, and he was not making a man's job of it. Suddenly, a gentleman in a Rolls Royce drew up alongside the field. The boy did not know the man and was surprised when the chap got out of the car and ordered him, 'Get off that tractor now and don't get back on it till I give you a ring!' Astonished, the boy went home. How this was explained to the farmer is unclear, but ten days later there was a phone call. It was from the man in the Rolls Royce; 'You can get back on that tractor now.' The boy did, and a perfect seedbed ensued. The moral? Farmers who can afford big motor cars know a thing or two about working strong land, and any boy that aspires to earn such wealth would do well to take notice of their advice.

But I had no limousine drawing up alongside my field. I only had the feel of the land beneath my boot leather, and an eye which noticed how the lumps of ploughed land crumbled into a fine tilth as I kicked them. It is usually a mistake to do this, but I consulted local opinion.

There was a sharp intake of breath from some who said the land was far too wet underneath and the 'hosses will up t' their 'ocks in mud.' Others thought the weather set fair and I should not hesitate another minute. This conflict of opinion is not a new phenomenon; I was once standing by a an old plough that was about to be auctioned and asked four old-timers who were standing by it whether they thought it more suited for light land or heavy? With one voice, two shouted heavy and two shouted light.

At the beginning of May we release the carthorses from their winter captivity and give them the freedom of the meadows. They have spent six dreary, dank months living in their stable by day (when not at work on the fields) and by night they have rested in a strawed yard, sheltered from the cold in a lean-to, and munched dry hay. They do not complain. In fact, if I were to turn them on to the barren winter meadows they would stand at the gate and plead to be brought back in.

By April they feel the spring coming. Instead of plodding aimlessly round the yard at night, they stand sniffing the air, sensing the rising of the sap and the succulence returning to the grass. They look longingly over the gates and wait for their freedom. Some years it comes earlier than others, but this year, with an acute shortage of winter rain, persistent cold winds and no artificial fertilisers to speed things up, our meadows are slow to grow. Liberation has been a bit late, but when it comes it is a moment to savour.

At first they are nervous, but as soon as they see the grass and the first of their huge feet hits the meadow they fling their heads down with the force of hammer on anvil to bury their noses in it. Their great teeth rip the grass from the earth, and I swear their eyelids flicker in ecstasy.

This state lasts for only a few minutes. Such is the delight of the fresh grass that they must celebrate in movement. One horse will start to trot round the field, flinging its head high. This will distract the other and together they will trot, faster with each circuit. One will turn on the spot and kick out playfully at its mate, who will brake sharply with a slither and gallop in the other direction. Then they pause, breathless, until overcome by the headiness of the occasion they charge again, probably in the other direction. The scene can appear violent, but if you know the horses you can tell their bodies are coursing with delight. It can last for half an hour: biting, kicking, bucking, galloping, munching, playing.

Then comes the collapse. To watch a horse the size of a Suffolk Punch fall to the ground is to see a heavyweight boxer turn suddenly into a ballet dancer. It happens very slowly. Their heads droop as though they are going to faint; then their legs go at the knees as if turned to jelly; but they are in controlled descent, for as soon as they reach a few inches off the ground they shift their weight to one side so as to land their bellies with hardly a bump. A ton of horse has come to rest. Then, with a mighty heave and grunt, they twist themselves on to their backs and rub and rub and rub until some climactic satisfaction overtakes them. Their insides must slosh from side to side, for the accumulated gas produced by the rapid intake of fresh grass comes bellowing out of their rear ends with a force sufficient to wake the dead in the next parish. While one horse is indulging in this massage, the other may still be at the gallop.

This is when the earth moves. You can feel it several fields away. You hear a rumble of galloping hooves, punctuated by the rasping report of a gaseous escape. You can keep your dawn chorus and your cuckoos; these are my harbingers of spring.

I am thinking of spring lambs, of Easter, and how our little farm can now claim to be a greetings card come to life. The latest batch of lambs started to arrive a week ago. Although my calendar has had 'Lambs from this date' inscribed on it for nearly five months, we were never convinced. We suspected the idle ram of having a permanent headache. He never looked remotely enthusiastic. But we owe him an apology: behind that indifferent stare burned a virile passion. His girls are now paying the price.

The problem with ewes which have not had lambs before is that they don't try very hard when it comes to the birth. They assume they are suffering indigestion, or perhaps constipation, and wander around rather stiffly putting a brave face on things. One of our ewes, half-way through giving birth, sprinted across to the trough for feeding time. The half-born lamb dangling from her at the time will now presumably be so traumatised that it lives in fear of the dinner gong.

When lambs are born without any bother, it is a delight to watch. Their confused little bodies plop onto the ground like a bundle of wet washing, and take just one breath before looking for Mother. Then they stretch their limbs and stagger to their feet, wobbling on all fours like a rickety table. One foot goes bravely in front of another and slowly they inch closer to the radiant warmth of the ewe. So begins the most vital expedition of their lives, to the teat.

Considering the ewes haven't had months thumbing through Mothercare catalogues and getting into the maternal frame of mind, they do get the idea remarkably quickly. The instant they have sniffed the lamb and confirmed it is theirs, they defend it with stamping feet if you approach too closely, and a head butt will meet any other ewe that seems intent on theft. Once mother and lamb have bonded, I move them into the family quarters.

I have divided the lambing pen so that one half has ewes about to lamb, and the other has ewes with lambs. As soon as a new ewe and her lamb join the family circle all hell breaks loose. They start sniffing the newcomer, confused as to whether the lamb might be theirs. If they decide it is not, instead of leaving it alone they butt it into the air till the poor little thing retreats, bleating. This forces its real mother to step forward to the defence, providing she is not occupied in sniffing another ewe's lamb and thinking it might be hers. The great revolving mass of sheep and lambs, all sniffing and butting each other, gyrates for about five minutes until families are reunited.

But for all the lambs that are born without any difficulty, it is the ones that don't make it that stick in the memory. We lost twins because the first-born got its head firmly wedged and its legs tangled. It happened with another ewe but this time I was there to help. Remembering the lessons at our local agricultural college, I greased my hand. For those lambing lessons we were given an appliance made out of plywood and rubber which represented the rear end of a sheep. To give it an authentic feel, the rubber bag was encased in warm water at sheep temperature, and filled with slimy jelly. A bicycle pump was attached to it and the whole thing could be inflated so that when you inserted your hand as if helping a lamb to be born, the tutor could give a quick stroke of the pump to simulate a contraction. It is not the sort of device to which innocents should be exposed.

The real thing is far more satisfying if you are successful; and deeply depressing when you are not. I am just back from the lambing pen after helping a ewe to give birth to her over-sized lamb. The lamb didn't make it. I blew down its mouth as a sort of kiss of life, tickled its nostrils with a straw. It didn't respond. It was a big strapping sort of lamb that deserved to frisk in the meadows. Half an hour before I had been sitting in the bottom of a wagon, enjoying the lambs at play. Now I had a dead one to bury.

But if you can't take the knocks you are a poor shepherd. My nineteenth-century *Cyclopaedia of Agriculture* says of shepherding, 'Owing to the nature of his work affording him time and opportunity for quiet thoughts, there has always been associated with shepherding much that is poetic and beautiful and good.'

True. Except that this novice shepherd finds the poetic bits followed so swiftly by action that I am a spinning mass of emotions. Coupled with ewes and fresh-born lambs spinning around their pens, these are dizzy days on the farm.

I know an old farmworker who lives alone in a cottage by a marsh. He lives simply, cooking his meal in a smoky old pot on an open coal fire, and when he is not boiling up food for himself, the pot goes on bubbling with potato peelings for the hens. His garden is neat and ruthlessly productive: beans, cabbages, spuds and doughty sprouts thrive there. He does not waste space on flowers except for a row of sweet peas, which he hands out to his lady admirers, who are numerous. He has been a friend of mine for a year, but this week he was the answer to my prayers.

My problems began a fortnight ago. At about four o'clock one morning, I sat bolt upright in bed and announced that I was going to have to cancel the seed potatoes. Not only that, the cows were going to have to go. It was all becoming too much. Then, sweating with anxiety, I remembered there were 20 tons of manure to spread, meadows to be harrowed, pigs to be moved. 'I'm cancelling the potatoes,' I shouted again, this time with a sob in my voice as I thrust my head into the pillow in the hope of sleep. But there was no relief. Executives would call this a nervous breakdown and bring in therapists, but I suspect that such sleepless nights are a regular feature of farming life. Anyway, I couldn't cancel the potatoes because they were on their way.

Inspired by a holiday postcard, I decided perhaps I ought to say my prayers. The postcard, a folksy affair from the Austrian borders, showed 'Saint Isidor, the Farm Labourer'. He was a talented ploughman and devout man of God, so highly regarded that while he was praying every day, angels would come and do his work for him. The painting shows him kneeling before his church while a beaming angel in a nightdress ploughs the land behind.

My wife, who has custody of the Dictionary of Saints, tells me that, being a typical farmer, St Isidor stoutly denied he had any help. But I have learnt humility. I admitted I needed an angel, said my prayer, and soon fell asleep.

I am wary of admitting to visions, lest I be bracketed with the reborn turquoise tracksuit brigade, but I awoke with the name of the old man of the marsh on my lips. Thank you, St Isidor. I can't imagine why I hadn't thought of him before. He would make an ideal potato-planting companion. Like much manual work on farms, potato planting has a biblical simplicity about it. But it is slow, tedious and back-breaking, and if there is any way of getting a little unbiblical jollity into it, the opportunity must be seized.

I ploughed the furrows while the old boy filled the baskets and hauled the seed. He started at one end, I at the other, and when we met in the middle there was always a cheery tale to be told. There was the story of how he chopped off the end of one of his fingers, took it to the surgery to have it sewn back on but was told the doctor would be out for at least an hour. 'Well, I weren't waitin' that long,' he said, 'so I chucked it away and went home fur m' tea.'

Tales told, we would stoop once more to the potato planting. From a distance, a passer-by might think we were bent in prayer. But only St Isidor would have recognised which of us was giving thanks, and which was the labouring angel.

Most farmers are men with hundreds of acres and battalions of machinery. They don't struggle up to their orchards with buckets of pig grub, as I do twice daily. They wouldn't think I was a farmer. If they bothered to give me any consideration at all they would think I was a crack-pot, or more likely an irritant who spreads this organic, nostalgic nonsense: a pest they wish they could spray against.

But some farmers would be more generous and call me a part-timer. This is not quite right either, for although it is true that I earn part of my living in other ways than off the land, it is that side of my work which feels part-time. Actually it comes as rather a restful treat after the struggle with the pig buckets.

If they really wanted to needle me they would call me a 'hobby farmer'. I met an estate agent who owned 600 acres and reckoned he was a farmer and I was a hobbyist. But he farms his land from behind his desk, and while he is driving around in his Japanese jeep waving detachedly at his farm, this so-called hobby farmer is out mending the fence the sheep are destroying. He'll have scanned his balance sheet, checked his feed conversion ratios, and glanced at the barley futures on the city pages while the alleged hobbyist is still struggling to get the rust off his aged Lister Blackstone swatch turner before hay-making.

I have now come to the conclusion that I am one of a rare breed. I am a peasant. A trainee peasant, at least. I just want to wrap my modest parcel of land around me and get on with it. It makes for an insular life with peculiar problems. Machines, fertilisers, and medicines now come in parcels too large for us to handle. I have a cow with lice: the smallest bottle of treatment I could buy was sufficient to dose fifty animals and cost over fifty quid. I think the cow was as shocked as I was, for when I told her she stopped itching immediately and hasn't rubbed herself since.

Small-scale farmers don't seem to fit into anybody's scheme of things. I glanced at one or two training schemes that were on offer, but they were all about operating machines that I had never heard of which wouldn't fit through our gates. Or else they were useless. One course offered farmers a day's tuition in *Improve your Telephone Selling Technique*. Peasants are ahead of that game already: the other day a lady rang up to order a couple of joints of pork and in conversation I persuaded her to have a pound of sausages as well. I would have had her taking the liver, had I not spied a horse which had slipped his halter and was heading for the wide blue yonder.

I have contracted an infectious disease and the symptoms are disturbing: you find yourself walking with a jaunty gait as if everything were well with the world; a song appears on your lips and a smile on your face where all winter has been a weary frown. Instead of worrying about what disasters may befall the budding crops, you see only how well the land looks, how straight the furrows. Songwriters would call it love; but the sheep and I know it is something different. It is nothing to do with the weather. In fact, after a deliciously mild spell we are once again raked by icy northerly winds that make cows and horses defiantly turn their backs in that direction. But despite the chill, an unmistakable feeling of elation is on us.

The sheep sensed it a couple of weeks before I did; and the little lambs sniffed it even before their experienced mothers. Yet it took two days of liberation from the lambing pens before the symptoms first appeared. Sheep do not like change, and even though they were freed from the enclosure of the farm-yard and put out to grass they still bleated pitifully to be brought home at night in the hope that delicious food might be laid before them in troughs. But lying at their feet was a rich feast, finer than any bucket could carry. The spring grass was shooting forth with vigour: packed with nourishment, if only they realised it. It would have been easy to have succumbed to their pleadings and brought them home had I not remembered a great truth I discovered tucked away in a shepherd's memoirs. 'Sheep,' he said, 'are not stupid. They just need time to think.' So I gave them time, and soon they were tucking in enthusiastically.

The effect of the grass on the lambs was dramatic. Made healthily plump by a rush of revitalised milk, they bounded round the field as if propelled by elastic bands. First they ran this way and that; and then, presumably having had time to think about it, decided it would be more fun to run a race. So began the Lambs' Grand National which seems to have its starting line somewhere near the trough and finishes eight acres away near the gate. Some just ran, others leaped along like liberated kangaroos and others, drunk on mother's milk, flung themselves into the air with such vigour that they landed facing the other way and fled backwards. It took them a long time to think that one through.

But my own feeling of well-being comes as much from the look of the land as from the antics of the lambs. I sowed the grass seed this time last year and watched its feeble attempts to grow as it took successive assaults from frost and, worse, drought. It never really grew at all last summer, merely raising sad wisps of fragile green that were never destined to flourish. The weakness of the grass was matched only by the strength of the weeds, and by the middle of the year I had a fine meadow of thistles, poppies, mayweed, nettles and docks. But no grass.

I was on the point of giving up, ploughing the field, and consigning the notion of organic growing to the back-burner. After all, had I wanted to apply chemicals to kill the weeds and fertilise the grass, I could easily have done so. Instead, I took advice from one of my aged farming text-books, and merely took the mower to it. The horses and I dragged that rackety old mower up and down for the best part of two days and then turned our back on the field, not even bothering to clear what we had cut. The weeds once more took hold, the grass maintained its modesty. I checked the text-book once again, and when the horses gave me a cold stare, asked a friend to do the second round with his tractor.

By mid September the magic started to work. The weeds had vanished, the grass had woken from its unnaturally long slumber. Back from the grave it is now as green and thick as the Wembley turf, with hardly a weed in sight. Is it any wonder that I am cheered, not only to see success snatched from the jaws of disaster, but to have the young lambs joining in the celebration? Add to that the contented cows who are sniffing the air and dreaming of days out at pasture; and the hard-working horses still shuffling around winter's strawed yards, but looking forward to their first mouthful of the scented grass they helped to grow.

Grass is springing and our spirits are high. If only the cart-horses and I could work out a way of harvesting that feeling and packing it in sacks, our fortunes would be made.

In a normal season, hay is made by mowing grass and allowing the sun to dry it. A good breeze helps, too. When it is dry on one side, you flip if over and allow it to cook gently on the other. After about five days it becomes hay and you put it in the shed.

When the going is good it is a pleasant enough business; especially if you are farming with horses, for the flipping-over the swathes of drying grass brings out heady scents that would never penetrate a tractor cab.

But June showed no sympathy, and it was becoming desperate. I was hoping to make hay out of my red clover crop which, although highly nutritious when dry, is a soggy sort of crop when freshly mown and badly needs heat.

'What you wanna do, boy,' said my consultant, aged eighty or so, 'is do what we used t' do. Yer wan' 'er cock that up!' So I did.

The weather forecast gave a promise of three dry days. If we could get it cut and partially dried, we would be able to build our cocks and allow the rest to take place within them. Cocks are miniature haystacks, loosely built. If you made a big stack of damp clover, it would go mouldy; if it is built around tripods with passages to allow the free flow of air, it can stand safely in the open for weeks. So the old boy told me.

On Thursday I got the horse-drawn clipper out of the barn and gave the Suffolk Punches a hearty breakfast. '… Expected to stay dry in the east till Saturday afternoon,' said the forecast. 'G'up,' I called to the horses and the rattle of the mower cut across the valley for all of half a minute. The crop was over-thick after the wet June, and the knife had clogged. It took five minutes to free. 'G'up,' and we clacked along. Then we jammed again. I felt the three dry days ebbing away and hardly 50 yards mown. I adjusted the mower to cut higher. 'G'up.' One horse shot forward like a bullet and the other didn't move. The harness had broken. Back to the stable, hot and very bothered, for more leather.

We cut three sides of the field and turned the horses to take the fourth. 'G'up.' They moved forward, but with hesitation and I don't blame them. Ahead lay a thick forest of Scotch thistles, each spine ready to torment a sweating horse's body. As we reached the clump the horses slowed, so the cutter jammed. It was lunchtime.

'... With showers breaking out in the east by Saturday morning,' the radio said. They'd moved the rain forward half a day! Lunch was grabbed and back to the field. We abandoned the thistly patch and set to on the rest. It was tea time.

'... With rain, heavy and thundery overnight on Friday in the east.' Again! With every sweating step we took, the weather forecasters were inching the deluge closer. Quite frankly, I didn't believe them. I rang a special number which gives a recorded weather forecast for farmers. It begins 0898 and my finger, still wobbly after a day on the mower, must have misdialled. I reached a panting lady who said, 'Hello there, Big Boy. Does your wife know you're calling me?'

I awoke the next morning to find the sun blazing and the cut clover much drier. The forecast was now for no rain till later that night. I took a horse and our vintage swath turner and turned every row so the damper underside was exposed to the sun. I sniffed the fragrance of the cooking clover, and scented victory in the air.

About four o'clock we set up our wooden tripods. The horse-rake dragged the clover into heaps and with forks we placed the heaps around the tripods, building them with care till they rose 8 feet from the ground, rounded on top but steep-sided to repel the rain. It looked like a primitive village: a sight not seen hereabouts for many decades, an ancient pattern back in the summer landscape.

We finished at half past ten, exhausted and aching, and I watched the late weather forecast. Rain was heading relentlessly our way – 'Downpours in the east tonight!' Happily we went to bed.

It is now four days since we finished, and it has not rained. I guess somebody else cocked it up, too.

Anyway, I have given up on weather forecasters. Over the years I have defended these skilled scientists from all who saw them as an easy target for jest and abuse; but no longer. I will not even insult a good piece of seaweed by bracketing it with them.

Let me explain that a week or so ago I cut a meadow with a view to making hay, and never had a more enjoyable couple of days. Newly sharpened and renovated, the clipper sliced through the sward without faltering; a gentle breeze wafted in from seaward filling the air with a salty tang.

The horses were enjoying it too. With a machine to pull that is in prime working order, the horses stepped out to give their best to the job and needed no guiding, other than at the corners, leaving me free to day-dream and enjoy the mingling scents of the sea, newly mown grass and cart-horse. Cutting grass for hay is not a task to be lightly undertaken. Without the certainty of a spell of settled weather, the grass will not dry and after a while begins to rot. With our precious lucerne, we can employ tripods as I recently described; but there is simply too much hay. Anyway, the forecast assured a dry spell and I had high hopes of being able to make hay in the traditional way by allowing it to wilt in the sun, turning it over to allow sun and breeze to dry both sides, and then spend an arduous but satisfying couple of days carting it home to build a monumental hay-stack.

It all worked according to plan; we managed several wagonloads and the stack rose steadily. I rang the weather forecast to see how long the weather was going to stay fine, but four forecasts, culled from telephone, radio and television, all promised an unexpected thundery spell of unsettled weather. This was bad news, but not too bad. It was to be followed by, and I quote the words which are music in the ears of any hay-maker, "high pressure building again from the south." A little shower does not matter: the hay quickly dries again. And so, believing I had got away with it, I looked forward to two more days of carting and the best stack of hay we had ever built.

Whoever issued those fateful words concerning the high pressure and rapidly settling weather had better not show himself on this farm. The skies were as settled as a hungry pig chasing a swill bucket. I dialled the recorded weather tapes, and screamed in the manner of a man losing his grip on reality. 'Where's the bloody high pressure?' I ranted. 'Do not pretend you have not heard me.' Not only did these disembodied voices not respond, they had the neck to change their tune like an entire orchestra swapping concertos. "With more heavy rain over the next few days ..." droned some girl with not a hint in

153

her voice that she had lied to me only twenty four hours before. Had she no shame?

So who can I now turn to when the weather has to be judged and farming operations planned ? As so often in the past, I have turned to history rather than trust the novelties of the late 20th century. On my shelves is a small booklet called *The Shepherd of Banbury's Rules* first published in 1670. I warn you the rules are complex; "If the wind return to the South within a day or two without rain, and turn Northward with Rain, and return to the south, in one or two days,as before, two or three times together after this Sort, then it is like to be in the South, or South West, two or three Months together, as it was in the North before. The Winds will finish these turns in a Fortnight."

It makes more weather sense than a lot I have heard lately.

Given that the process of sanctification is a long and tortuous one, I will settle for a statue or even a nice blue plaque for the candidate I have in mind. It is not someone I know, but his writings have been an inspiration to me; and if he had a few more disciples amongst modern commercial farmers, agriculture might be able to hold its head a little higher. Having said that, give me seven days before I deliver a final verdict; but I am pretty confident I've got the right man.

Newman Turner wrote three books at the end of the 1940's. knowing nothing of what is currently called organics and preferring to describe his practices as "fertility farming." I have made his books my bible.

If I sound besotted with the man it is because I have witnessed one of his miracles, and may be about to participate in another. Two years ago, depressed beyond belief by a field of newly sown grass seed that was being smothered by every weed in God's creation, I came upon Turner's chapter smugly titled *How I made a Meadow with a Mower.* He too had sown his grass and got in return an abundant crop of weeds. Being of little faith, my solution was to plough the disaster under so that I could start again.

But Turner did not give up as easily. He took a mower to his field, sliced off the blossoming weeds, and waited. He was rewarded with a sward of grass which would do justice to the Centre Court. With

154

a prayer on my lips, I did the same. With our horse-drawn clipper we trundled round the field and simply left the clippings to rot. Within a month a miracle had taken place: I had turned water into wine. Thistles, rape, nettles had all gone and fresh shoots of young grass were now tall enough to sway gently in the breeze. Ever since then I have turned to Newman Turner's sermons on the value of herbs in meadows and followed his teachings; he intones "Upon a basis of humus, nature sows her seeds …" and then lays down his commandments for fertility. Such is my faith that I have just put his scriptures to the ultimate test.

I have a fine crop of lucerne this year which is one of our most valuable crops. It grows with abundance and when made into hay delivers the most sweet-smelling, nutritious fodder any beast could ask for. Believe me, this is Michelin 3 star stuff. The only problem is that it grows so vigorously that we must take three crops a year which means a first cut in mid-May, a notoriously showery time of year in which to dry the lucerne and make hay. But Turner never lost any sleep over it.

"Now I can make hay … as green as the best dried grass. Each year, instead of greyer hair I have greener hay."

This is very beguiling talk to a man like me who has a field of shimmering lucerne, a week's holiday looming, and a weather forecast as black as Alice's, the pig's, snout. Turner advocates making the hay on tripods; eight foot high wigwams of grass which allow fresh, drying breezes to blow through them. We have done this before in the very final stages of making our hay. Not only has it been effective, but for a few weeks every year we have our own little Stonehenge as these monolithic towers of drying grass cast their primeval shadows. But what we of little faith have not dared to do before is act with the urgency that Turner demands. He tells us that a mere 18 hours after cutting the grass is the time to be forking it onto the tripods. We have never dared to act so swiftly and have spent nervous days, if not weeks with our fingers crossed, hoping the weather holds. Usually, it doesn't

Unless you have made hay you cannot appreciate how radical this hasty approach to be. It is as if a cookery writer had declared that a mere five minutes was all a loaf of bread needed to bake; or a vintner suggesting port was best drunk straight after bottling. But this saint did not let me down before and so I shall follow him even unto every corner of the field of lucerne. The tripods are standing, the pitchforks dusted off. The thunder-clouds are gathering and my holiday tickets are booked. Our crop is now in the hands of Another.

Then, to dampen my spirits, Mr. Watkins, who lives not far from here, got in touch to tell me how he slaved to make hay on tripods – 'back-breaking but satisfying' – only to end up with 'hay that looked like knitting needles.' He tells of being thwarted by the gale which sprang up the instant they left the field for a well earned supper, and had them scurrying back to the field to tie the escaping grass back onto the tripods. Mr. Watkins is of the firm opinion that tripoding may be fine for the 'cloud-cuckoo-land of Turner, but not in East Suffolk.'

I have to admit that I had my doubts too. The field was mown in glorious sunshine and allowed to wilt for at least two days having been turned over once to allow the sun and the breeze to attack both sides of it. I cut it on the Sunday and decided it would go on the tripods that Friday. I happened to catch the lunchtime forecast on Wednesday and was shocked rigid by a drastic change in their opinion. Words like "torrential" and "flooding in places" were littered throughout their damp little forecast. I hit the phone. The forecast was broadcast at 1:30; by 2:30 I had five blokes on the field wielding pitch-forks as if to hold back some overwhelming natural disaster.

'Clung!' said my old friend Dilly who had been aroused from behind the Daily Mirror and hauled into a fast car. 'That ol' grass be clung!' He meant it was too damp, soggy, floppy; it is an adjective frequently used hereabouts to describe not only limp lumps of grass, but people as well. 'It will be alright,' I told him, attempting to inflect my voice with a confidence that my heart did not hold. It is difficult to explain to someone who was making hay when beer was a penny a pint that, although you greatly respect his opinion, you believe it to be wrong on the basis of something you have just read in a book, that is how you come to get a reputation for being clung yourself. So I kept my mouth shut and my pitchfork moving and by half past five as the clouds gathered in the western sky, the last tripod was thankfully topped-up.

There was no gale; but what the weather lacked in ferocity it made up for in dampness. For three days it cascaded upon the tripods till the very ground round them was squelchy underfoot. After a few days I bravely slid my hand beneath the layers of hay on the tripods, and found it emerged sodden up to the cuffs on my shirt. Sorry, Mr. Turner. There was no point taking any action, for there was simply nothing to do. But on a scorching day last week, I decided we had better nerve ourselves and cart the lucerne to the yard and build a stack – if it was worth it.

I have had few greater joys in my short farming career than the moment when my fork cut through the bleached outer layers of dried lucerne to reveal, hidden beneath, a rich seam of perfectly preserved fodder. It was all that Turner had promised. It did not have that cooked look that hay takes on when it has been cruelly dried under a blazing sun, "the goodness having been burnt out of it" as Turner suggested. But it had a preserved quality; it had a life about it which had been fossilised by the slow and steady drying effect of having been lifted off the ground onto these miraculous tripods and gently dried by the action of the breeze alone. It had a preserved vitality which you could sense would re-emerge the moment it hit a cow's palate. The torrential rain had made no difference to it: the outer layers acted as a thatch and soon dried in the sunshine.

But the smell was even better. It had the malty aroma of Horlicks, the freshness of a recently trodden daisy, the perfume of a Chardonnay. If ever there was vintage hay, this was it. If cattle belonged to good clubs, they would surely lay down a few bales of this stuff to guzzle after dinner ten years hence. I still go out to the stack, and sniff it. I toast Newman Turner who, if not posthumously ennobled, should be put at least on some kind of pedestal, a three-legged one, of course.

It may be the recent plethora of wartime anniversaries that has prompted this, but I find that my approach to farming is becoming increasingly Churchillian; a bit more bulldog and a bit less poodle. Take last Friday for example. I sat at the kitchen table as the great man might have sat in his bunker; beside me was Farmer White. We were discussing the hay, yet again. It was a conversation riddled with tales of blood, sweat and tears.

I am sure you are sick of hearing of my problems making hay this year but to any leader facing a battle, single-mindedness is essential. And paranoia is apparently not uncommon at haysel, as haymaking time is known in the eastern counties. An anonymous reader kindly sent me a delightful book called *A Pullet on the Midden* in which Rachel Knappet describes her farming experiences in the 1950's. It takes a very short time for her to come to the conclusion that, "All farmers are temperamental at certain times of year. When it rains and all the hay is cut … the boss goes about looking like thunder cloud with a hard line between his eyes and a snappy retort for anyone who is brave enough to speak to him. The men have a stoical philosophy which supports them under the hail of curses that fills the air at these times." Well, stoicism is running out fast in this family. My enraged wife declared last week that 'the only way to get any attention round here is to be a lump of dead grass.'

But despite the travails of making hay, I am now managing to rise above it; be more statesmanlike about my farming, draw on the example set by our leaders and look on events as battles that we must win and not hurdles placed there mischievously by nature.

And so, desiring to be a leader of events rather than a victim, I called Farmer White, my Eisenhower, into the bunker to discuss D Day; D standing for Desperation. The hay had by now had so much rain poured upon it that it was almost as sodden as the day it was mown some eight days previously. We had decided to surrender. Troops were standing by under the command of Farmer Watson, who was to roll the stuff into huge circular bales with his special machine and stuff it in black plastic bags. This constituted a managed, if rather shameful retreat. It was unlikely ever to make decent fodder but at least I would be rid of it.

Then, we listened to the weather forecast. Montgomery of the Met Office threw a whole new light on our desperate situation with a forecast of settled weather. I know I have been led astray before in this way but a desperate man will clutch at any straw, even a sodden one.

One day to dry, Eisenhower and I decided, and then cart it to the stack: victory dragged from the jaws of defeat and all that. I shoved my mug of tea aside, my jaw already going slack in anticipation of a rousing speech. Victory pumped through my veins. I looked across at the damp field of grass, not believing it could ever make hay. 'It could be our finest hour,' I thought to myself.

I rang Farmer Watson who, thankfully, was wearing his hearing-aid, and told his battalions to stand down; then I started to raise an army of my own. I rang Dilly first. Dilly was in the Western Desert. He knows how it has to be. He answered the call. 'Give us the tools and we will finish …' Then he thought again, 'No, I'll bring m' own fork. Better than yours.'

And so within a day of that fateful decision, my Dad's Army of helpers went into battle and swept the hay into the most glorious stack this farm has ever seen. On the scale of world events, this has been a small skirmish but it has meant a great deal to me. It is easy to turn your back on farming problems when, these days, there are so many courses of action to extract you from the hole you are in. It would have been no problem for me simply to buy-in the hay we needed for the winter. But I chose not to, for those whose farming practices have provided my inspiration had no choice in these matters, so neither must I. Tempting though it is at times, we shall never surrender.

Compared with most farmers who need to get as much from their land as they can achieve in order to survive, I do not ask a lot of this little farm. I give the land and the stock as much tender, loving care as it needs. I have wooed it endlessly with fences, gates, barns and ditches. We have put our organic hearts into the natural fertilising of the land and never spared the stock their feed, no matter how expensive or hard won. And now it is beginning to pay off: the farm is beginning to get a twinkle in her eye. Weaned from its previous chemical regime, the soils are showing every sign of recovering from their chemical addictions. The stock are healthier too; I have not had to take my grim grave-digger's spade to excavate a resting place for a ewe for at least a year. But for all the bunches of red roses that I have blandished on my mistress, there are ways in which she shows signs of fickleness. Ingratitude.

I am referring to the farm machinery, or at least a couple of items from our battery of aged farm implements. Let us take first of all the Lister Single-Cylinder Petrol Engine (circa 1950). If working, it is a useful little engine; light enough to be dragged around the farm to drive the hay elevator or oat-roller. These engines have a certain charm. Always painted green, they are to be seen at rallies emiting an irritating put..put..put..hiccup..put, while the onlookers marvel as if the internal combustion engine had just been invented. The trouble with my engine is that there is rather too much hiccup and not enough put..put. In the hands of our local engineer, Mr. Jackson, she runs like a Bentley but she knows he is the sort of man who can perform with a spanner what Christian Barnard used to manage with a scalpel. But as soon as I get her home, the spark goes out of her. I crank for hours till my head spins but she will not go. I send for Mr. Jackson. He primes her with fuel and then spins her no more than twice and way she roars like a lion, thundering with energy, put..put..putting me in my place.

For the time of year it has been strangely quiet in the cornfields. Two sounds have been missing: the gobble of the combine harvesters as they march across the fields, and the low murmur of a farmer cursing the weather.

It has been a terrific harvest, any farmer will tell you that. One chap, sitting in my kitchen said 'I can't quite believe it. We got the combine out of the shed, dusted it off, worked steadily through the fields, and put it away again.' Simple as that. No thunderstorms, no drenched corn, no soggy straw to handle. It is going to be a very peaceful close to a traditionally busy month on the land.

This easy harvest, though, is not entirely to do with the weather. The truth is that the growing of corn is now in the unromantic hands of agricultural engineers and scientists, and less in the lap of the gods. Crops are fed and watered by God's almighty hand, but only up to a point. After that the machines take over. Until the invention of the horse-drawn binder in the 1850's which cut the corn, bundled it, tied a string round it to create a sheaf, and then dropped it on the ground in one continuous action, corn was still being harvested by men with scythes. Brian Moore, a retired farm worker in east Suffolk and only 67, remembers cutting the edges of the fields with a scythe. 'We never started till the first week in August. Went right through till the end of October. There were eight of us on the farm and six extras for harvest. We had to stand the sheaves of corn up to dry, and turn them over if it rained.' It was truly hard labour, and the chance of fine weather lasting for the many weeks of the slow harvest were slim. At least a late harvest meant help from the harvest moon. These days, on early August nights you might see combine harvesters working by the light of a full moon; but the traditional harvest moon is the one that falls in September. It is a measure of the way modern machinery has nudged the seasons. Many of the old farm-workers shunned any kind of mechanisation. Brian remembers one old man, standing in a field with his scythe, remarking that these new-fangled combine harvesters were 'no more than a load of old treacle tins.'

Now, the treacle tins are in charge. The annual lengthy drama in which a small army of determined men faced overwhelming fields of corn has been replaced by a quick sketch in which one man in an air-conditioned cab harvests many more acres in an hour than that gang of men managed in a day only sixty years ago. It has made harvest a less chancy business, but it has robbed rural life of a camaraderie that came from fighting the common enemy in the days when farmers talked of "winning" the harvest. These days, with not only the help of advanced machinery but an armoury of chemical sprays to preserve the crop from all its enemies, and great humming grain driers which save any dampness from mattering, it is hardly a contest. Neither is it a matter of life or death, as it used to be: when farmers in the developed world these days speak of poor harvests, they mean slender profits and not empty bellies.

But there is a hunger for some connection with the old seasons, which means that in country places, in schools and churches, the traditional harvest festival has survived. Brian Moore's wife, Connie, who came to Suffolk as a land girl half a century ago, says that both church and chapel on that day are as well attended as she can ever remember. If the produce on display is anything to go by, congregations seem to be as willing to raise the song of harvest home to thank the Almighty for his gift of Tesco baked beans as they do to praise him for the fruits of the fields.

Yet nearly all other harvest traditions have become victims of the lonely life farmers lead, now that machines and not men are the victors on the harvest field. How many farmers still give a harvest supper to thank the workers in the fields? It is difficult in these days of contract labour, when the lad who drove the combine has probably moved on to a motorway-widening scheme.

Tucked away in a dusty corner of the newspaper last week was a report of a crime committed in North Yorkshire. Apparently, in the dead of night, thieves armed with forks raided a field of potatoes and made off with the entire crop. May I make a plea? If anyone knows the identity of these villains, or can give any information as to where they might be hiding, will they kindly give them my address? If it would help, I shall leave forks and spades by the roadside, and some sacks too. I'll even muzzle the dog.

You will gather that we are in the midst of the potato harvest, and the mangel-wurzels are developing that ready-to-be-picked look too. Farming seems to go in phases. I remember the early part of the year when the stock were in the yards and having feed brought to them, I spent months on end with a pitchfork over the shoulder till my neck muscles developed a groove.

Then, in the spring, came the rolling phase when I did nothing but walk up and down the land with the horses, rolling clods; then it was hoeing. Now we're into the backbreaking phase of plucking roots from the ground. To find the entire crop wafted away in the night would be cause for celebration.

I should not really complain: last weekend several hundred people turned up and picked most of my potatoes for me and paid for the privilege. Like all my good ideas, it was someone else's. I remember him saying that if you got a good site near a road and invited people to come and pick their own as they followed the horses along the furrow, you'd draw a crowd.

It worked. I stuck up a few posters, promised potatoes fertilised with only farmyard manure, and elbowed my way on to our local radio station to plug our slogan, 'Follow the horses along the furrow and hope to God what you're picking up is a potato!' Eat your heart out, Saatchi's. Sunday morning dawned bright, and with the kettle boiling for 10p cups of tea and the cheese ready sliced for the ploughman's lunches, I waited nervously. By way of insurance I hired some pickers so that if no one turned up, at least the day wouldn't be wasted.

I needn't have bothered. Even before the horses were harnessed a queue was forming. Children, youths, grandmothers and gentlemen of the cloth stood poised with an array of plastic bags, buckets, and a look in their eye that I have only seen in the few minutes before the start of the Harrods sale.

I called to the horses and our vintage potato spinner inched forward. It is an elderly brute of a machine that cuts beneath the ridges of earth and then, with a series of rotating fingers, spits the spuds out on to the ground.

We had gone only a few yards before the crowd descended on the furrow like gulls following the plough. At the ends of the ridges where the soil is shallower, the potatoes were smaller and there were long faces, but as we worked our way into the crop, giant footballs flung through the air as the spinner moved onwards.

Mothers dumped their babies and scrabbled among the clods of earth like Scarlett O'Hara. The professional pickers watched in disbelief. I developed a barrow-boy's patter. 'Come on, ladies and gentlemen, you won't find a fresher spud than these 'ere. C'mon, ten pence a pound.'

The day was a great success. Customers were delighted, horses flattered by relentless patting and cooing. The field is bare except for six rows. And now I must face those last few rows alone with no willing helpmates, giggling children or determined old ladies. If the felons wish to pay me a call, we have several left-over ploughman's lunches to offer them.

My heart sank at the thought that, in just a few short months, it will be lambing time again. Somehow, I always envisage that as the current task in hand is completed there will be some kind of break, in which the farm will be at perfection and I can idly stroll and admire it. I thought things might be quiet after hay and before harvest: they were not. I felt sure that once the corn was in we could relax; but I am now getting up a head of steam about starting autumn ploughing.

But the relentless cycle of the farming year has its compensations. Tonight, for example, I took a stroll to look at the cows, and swooping low over the deep ditch that runs the length of the farm was my old friend the barn-owl. I doubt I have seen him since last March but he knows the barn is filling with corn, and the mice will soon be emerging from the fields to take up residence. Our barn is his local take-away: he usually drops in about six for his supper and returns home to a tree I know the whereabouts of, but refuse to divulge to anyone. I am thrilled to see him again.

I am sick of the sight of mangel-wurzels. I hate them, loathe them. I have been grabbing them from the ground which they have been reluctant to leave, flinging them into a cart which has groaned under their weight, pulled by a cart-horse which was hardly able to keep his feet in the filthy mess the mangels have left behind. In past years, it has always been a chore, but never the torture that lifting this year's crop entailed. We have hauled nearly thirty tons of the lousy things, all by hand, and they now lie in a huge, straw-covered mound. I cannot even bring myself to look at them; we certainly do not speak.

Admittedly, I did not start the mangel lifting in the finest of health. A bad cold had settled on my chest, shivering chills alternating with fevers; but you cannot tell this to the weather, which was lying in wait with its icy fingers poised to scatter a frost over the field of mangels and reduce them to pulp. A touch of ground-frost will not harm them, for the leaf acts as a canopy and takes the edge off the chill; but a biting air frost will scar them and turn them to that same squashy and stinking consistency of an aged cucumber forgotten in the fridge.

But there were other pressures too. Dilly was on the phone. 'Best get them up boy! That's gettin' on.' It was too. We were into the second week in November and anyone else foolish enough to grow mangels had already lifted them and put them safely to bed for the winter. Cold or no cold, we set to work.

The first half hour was fine. Dilly slashed the green tops and hauled their roots while we went behind with the horse and cart, flinging them onto it. Then, my weakened physical state took over and those juices which ones body produces in abundance at times like these started to flow like the Mississippi in full spate. As I bent to lift the mangel, they slopped forward filling my forehead, and when I rose to fling the root into the cart, they sloshed backwards till the inside of my head became like the swimming pool of the QE2 in the middle of an Atlantic storm.

Dilly was loving it; cheerily he swiped the tops, but always with accuracy, for the mangel must not be cut in any way or it will effect a kind of bleed and gradually grow rotten from the point the incision was made. If it is in contact with other mangels, as it would be in the heap, it would turn them rotten too. A vindictive little beast is the mangel; if it is going to suffer it makes sure everyone else does as well. But there I go again, bitterness and recrimination.

I always hoped that when I took up farming I would somehow forge a mystical union with the land, sky and wind and gain an understanding of the four great seasons of the year. It has not worked out quite as I expected.

I suppose it is writers who are to blame for raising false expectations. My mind was filled with Dick the Shepherd blowing his nail, and Shelley's wild west wind, breath of autumn's being, and Tennyson's moans of doves in immemorial elms, Not to mention "There's a whisper down the field where the year has shot her yield, And the ricks stand grey to the sun, Singing:- 'Over then, come over, for the bee has quit the clover, And your English summer's done.' (Kipling).

I would love to be able to say that I have no further need for clock or calendar; that the rhythms of my life are dictated by the migration of the sun through the heavens. It would make me genuinely happy to tell you that the moans of the dove had supplanted the Budget as a marker in the year, or that it was the quitting of the bee from the clover which spurred me into gathering fuel for the bleak midwinter, instead of a special offer of bulk heating oil.

Instead, I find that increasingly the turning of the seasons is marked ever less by the events of nature and more by the mutterings of man. It was a casual encounter in the village which crystallised all this in my mind. It has been bitterly cold this last couple of weeks, cold for June anyway. The wind has been set in the north and the poor cows and horses who lost their winter coats back in early May when it looked as though a blistering summer was on the cards, now find themselves cruelly cheated and spend long days under the hedge with their backs to the wind. 'More like April' I cried to someone I met in the street, turning up my collar to deflect the drizzle. 'We always say that,' he replied, 'every year, the same. We moan that we've had to put the heating back on, as if we'd never had to do it ever before. But it's the same every year. Every year!'

Thinking back, it is amazing how the same conversations are held every year, at roughly the same time, and always on the same subject – far more reliable than bees leaving clover. Take the business of the leaves of the sugar beet plant. This topic of conversation is almost as punctual as the Queen's *Christmas Message*. Round about the middle of May, someone will tell you that the sugar beet looks a "bit behind." It is never forward, always behind. They will then tell you that 'father 'allus reckoned that the leaves of the sugar beet should meet across the rows by the date of the county show.' As the Suffolk Show always falls at the end of May and the leaves look some distance from an embrace, there is much shaking of heads, as if the end of the world had just been declared official. For all I know, since that bit of folklore was established they may have moved the show back a few weeks. But the discussion must still be held, every year, on the plight of the crop .

Then, again in the spring, we have the ritual of standing at the edge of the meadow, moaning about how the grass does not seem to be growing properly. This is irrespective of the state of the actual crop. Somehow, we dare not let ourselves be optimistic. If I dare to mention, casually, that the grass is looking 'fine', someone is certain to say, 'yes, it's not too bad. But it's not growing properly yet.' The blades of grass could be high enough to tickle that chap's armpits, but the sowing of doubt has become such a yearly occurrence that I now suspect that the seasons will not advance till the ritual has been played out.

'Time those sheep were sheared!' That's another one. As soon as any warmth is felt in the spring sunshine, someone will look at the flock and remark that 'they'm be ready to have them coats off.' Had I followed that advice every time it was given I would have had a flock of sheep which would have qualified for the Government's cold weather allowance. had they not died in the meantime. Shearers will tell you that there is a right time to take a fleece from a sheep and it is when the oil is beginning to rise in the wool. It appears to have little to do with what the thermometer might suggest. But, nevertheless, every year for the last five I have been urged to take early shears to the flock. Every year I have ignored the advice. But now I know that until I have heard those words and suffered a subsequent cold snap, spring cannot possibly turn to summer.

So forget that stuff about larks and cuckoos and spring not being far behind; poets clearly spend too much time indoors. Chronicle the conversations instead.

"Hark, summer's near, the farmers moan
Bewailing unshorn sheep and tardy seed
Rejoice! The summer surely must be close
'Tis grumbling, not the sun, that makes the seasons speed."

(Heiney)

THIRTEEN

I can't remember how the idea occurred, but it suddenly became clear to us that what we had in our little farm was a setting for the perfect Nativity play. And so it became an annual event, and never passed without incident.

As farmyards go, ours takes some beating when it comes to staging a nativity play. We have lambing shelters thatched with straw, lowly cattle-sheds, and mangers in which babies can be lain. We even have cattle who will low on cue, and sheep with which shepherds can abide. We tried it last year and old ladies wept at the simple beauty of it. This year it was my turn to shed tears.

The trouble has been the rain. Our normally dry and cosy yard had become a swamp, and as the flood-waters rose and notices were being pinned up in shop-windows across the county making our nativity play inevitable, mighty dread filled my troubled mind. I convened an emergency meeting of the Three Wise Men; Farmer White, the lad who drives his big digger, and me. Then, as if things weren't bad enough already, word came through from the village that Joseph had got 'flu.

Actually, the cast was becoming a bit of a problem. Finding the children was the easy bit, for they were provided (like all good emergency supplies) by the local branch of the British Red Cross to whom we were donating all the ticket money. The admirable Mrs. Low had marshalled them, rehearsed them, and persuaded them out of attending a party at the local pub which clashed directly with our nativity play. I regret to say that a few shepherds did fall for the pub's invitation, but that is shepherds for you. We had some good recorder-playing siblings from up the road instead. No, the kids were fine; it was the livestock that was the worry. I needed a cart-horse to bring Mary and Joseph to Bethlehem. Prince is too young and lively, and was quite likely to have bolted past the inn with the result that Jesus would have been born somewhere between here and the outskirts of Ipswich. Both Star and Blue are up to the part but yonder Star, deliberately I think, rolled for so long in a patch of particularly noxious mud that there was never any hope of getting him clean enough to go on stage. Blue got the role. I decided that I would not break it to him at this stage that he would also be cast as the Three Kings' camel.

All that remained was to choose the cow who was to pay homage to the infant Jesus. Sage, the white cow, was the obvious choice but she seemed a little sniffy when I mentioned the idea. Last year she bridled visibly when the radiant Angel Gabriel appeared: if anyone is going to be snow-white, gasped-at, and lauded with trumpets it is going to be her, or she isn't playing. The job fell to Bilberry, as the only one who could safely be led on a halter. I decided Dilly, the farm-worker to whom all disasters have already befallen, was the man to lead her in: whatever happened he would cope. Then I got a call: Dilly had the flu.

It is wisely said that once you are in a hole you stop digging, but the Three Wise Men were determined to do exactly the reverse. Desperate to rid ourselves of the ever-rising tide, we decided to reverse the Moses trick and dig a huge chasm to see if the rain-water would disappear down it. It did. A miracle. We filled the hole with stones and hoped our problems were behind us. I congratulated Farmer White for parting the seas, and prepared for the holy birth. Merry gentlemen we became, nothing would us dismay. Then it started to rain.

Past three o'clock, on a foul rainy evening. And the play was due to start at four. The lighting chap doubted it was safe; if there were going to be any stars in the bright sky, it would be when the rising water hit his fuse-box. I almost decided to cancel. And then, how silently, how silently, a wondrous gift is given. The low, heavy cloud lifted, the rain ceased and the glimmering light of the setting sun fell upon the farm-yard. We looked at each other, joyful and triumphant. Vernon, the narrator, arrived. He was to perch on the rails of the cattle-yard, telling the story while the children acted it out. I will not say much of Vernon except that he has a strong voice, lives in a caravan in a wood, makes pegs, and arrived improbably dressed in a flowing gown which once adorned the waxwork of Martin Luther in Madame Tussauds. Method actors! Tony arrived to play the Angel Gabriel, complete with trumpet and newly composed fanfares. We asked him to come dressed in white, but did not reckon on it being a pair of overalls stamped Nuclear Electric. He had, however, carefully concealed the logo with tinsel. We thought at least he would glow naturally.

At four o'clock sharp, we started. The melodeon player quietly gave us *In the Bleak Midwinter*, and the air noticeably chilled as the sun disappeared. 'And it came to pass ...' intoned Vernon, whereon the cattle decided it was time that they should be heard. Never has so much mooing been made by so few. Vernon struggled and the audience stifled their giggles. It is probably the first time in history that the line 'and a decree went out from Caesar Augustus that all the world should be taxed,' has got a laugh.

The horse came in smartly and delivered Mary and Joseph, the children sang *Away in a Manger*. It was not until *The First Noel* that the lump came in my throat. I have worried about this filthy yard for weeks, spent anxious nights worrying what would happen if the frenzied cow bolted into the audience, or if nobody enjoyed themselves. But now, with the sickle moon looking down upon us, the dusk descending, the cart-horse standing almost to attention, and a crowd belting out 'born is the king of I..i..israel', I could have cried.

And I would have done, had I not suddenly remembered that there was no gold, frankincense and myrrh for the three singing Kings to deliver. I grabbed three huge mangel-wurzels from the heap and thrust them into the Kings' fists. 'Put them in the manger' I said. Then it was the turn of the cow to pay homage to the baby Jesus. No! If that cow sees those mangels lying in the manger, there will be no holding her. But she did not spot them, and instead spent her time mooing at the other cows, who mooed back at her and most of the way through *Oh Come all Ye Faithful.*

And that is the story of our nativity play this year, except you may be wondering why Alice, the Large Black sow, has not made an appearance. Well, she was asked and declined. She is no fool. She knows that when we clear the yard much of that straw will be coming her way to make that chilly sty cosy for the winter; and those three mangel-wurzels will surely be hers too: she counted them out and she will count them back again. And the surplus sprouts, pudding and bread sauce too will be heading her way. No one on this farm will miss out on the feast of Stephen.

And now I am able to sit and write, and reflect on it. Luck, broadly speaking, was on our side. The soprano did not fall off the straw-stack as, without as much as a wobble (creditable since she was thirty feet in the air and the stack is a bit on the rickety side), she sang all the verses of *In the Bleak Midwinter.* This occupied those precious few moments between the setting of the sun (after which we dared not let the unaccustomed audience stumble from their seats on bales of straw) and the falling of total darkness (before which we dared not start the action). She did not even allow herself a giggle as the heifer chimed in with an ear-splitting mooo on the higher notes. The audience were not only transfixed by this celestial vision of a beautiful girl singing from the darkening clouds, but were also hemmed-in on all sides by cart-horses, cattle and sheep. Heaven above and hell all around them.

The narrator climbed on to a farm wagon and the story unfolded. The innkeeper (ten years old) gave much passion to his part, inspired by sheer delight at being able to tell his younger sister (the Virgin Mary) there was no room for her at his inn, no way. The massive brown frame of Blue, the Suffolk Punch, lumbered from the darkness and stole the scene as he hauled Mary and Joseph to their stable. The shepherds piped, and were sore amazed (as well they might be) by the apparition of our teenage Gabriel on the stack with a trumpet, apparently playing a cross between the *Coronation Fanfare* and the *Last Post*.

But while we all sang *The First Noel*, an unseen hitch occurred. Derek the horseman, who has probably never taken part in a theatrical event in his life, was supposed to take the horse and cart round the back, unhitch him and bring him in again bedecked with gold and gifts as the Three Kings' camel.

It is fortunate that Derek is a man of even temper, for at this point he and his camel could easily have got the hump. The only way round the farm buildings was blocked by a latecomer's car; he had to haul the reluctant cart-horse at top speed down the lane so he could cut across the field and still make it in time for the Three Kings' entrance. My wife spotted his dilemma and signalled the accordion player to do more verses. The narrator intoned, '… and far away, in the East, three wise men …', as the lumbering horse was forced into a near-gallop down the lane and the heavy clatter of steel shoes on roadway split the air.

Gabriel socked us another unusual fanfare, and by the time we had all got through *We Three Kings* with the baby in the real manger, the cow mooing, the sheep bleating and the Suffolk Punch standing magnificently to attention, it is fair to say there was not a dry eye in the house.

'The true spirit of Christmas,' wept one lady as she stumbled through the straw in the darkness. 'Moving, very very moving,' muttered another. An elderly but vital lady of ninety-three announced she was the great-grandmother of Jenny who had sung on the straw-stack, and that four generations of her family had been there to see it.

It was profitable: we raised £250 (all for the British Red Cross) and I seem to have done all right too. In order to spare our visitors a slow drowning in mud, a couple of local farmers donated straw to spread all over the yard. It is still there and is ready for the sheep, who will shortly be coming in to lamb. Without a hundred pairs of feet to kick it around, it would have been a sweaty job to spread it.

The Scrooge in me returning, I am planning another such event. Perhaps at Easter, we shall do the Stations of the Cross. I shall ask the audience each to carry a stake and process around the farm. Every time the script demands it, they will hammer it religiously into the ground. If it should so happen that they follow the line of the new fence I am planning, so much the better.

I hope the vicar didn't notice, but during the carol service the other night I was shifting as nervously as a troubled schoolboy. It was simply that the carols struck home in a way they never had in the days before I became a farmer. In nearly every hymn, a verse or a phrase set me off on an anxious train of thought, each one leading back to the farmyard.

No sooner had the boy soprano cut the air with his 'Once in royal ...' than we arrived at the lowly cattle shed. As the proud owner of several cattle sheds of the most lowly state imaginable, I did not find any comfort in being reminded of the work, and money, needed to keep them standing until next Christmas. As for 'Where a mother laid her baby /In a manger for a bed ...', it suddenly came to me that it was in the woodworm-ridden old cattle manger that I had left the spare breast for the plough. I've been looking for that for a week. Ah, the plough! It was a tradition in these eastern parts that good ploughmen should have turned all their land by Christmas Day, and to bring them luck for the following year, they would sleep on Christmas Eve with the breast of the plough beneath their beds. The congregation had reached 'And our eyes at last shall see him ...' by the time I had been through all the parcels of land that were still unploughed. If I'm in bed with the plough by Easter I shall be lucky. Feeling weak at the thought, I was glad when the vicar asked us to be seated.

But there was no rest. One lesson later *In the Bleak Midwinter* was announced, and the organist attacked the opening notes with an enthusiasm that suggested he hadn't been forking twenty loads of horse-muck that morning. '... Earth stood hard as iron, water like a stone.' I shuddered – a mighty dread had filled my troubled mind. In a big freeze-up, which is bound to come some time, gallons of drinking water will have to be carried bucket by bucket from house to farmyard. It comes to us via an electric pump in a well and if the power lines are down I shall be the one who has to tell the thirsty horses, cows, pigs and piglets that water is like a stone. Peace and goodwill will soon evaporate in an unseasonal display of foot-stamping and snorting.

'We three kings ...' intoned the vicar. Not much better. To be truthful, I've had a bellyful of wise men out of the east. I suspect there is a roving pack of retired farmworkers who hunt me down, not to dispense wisdom, but merely to haunt and undermine me. They stand watching me plough, and ignore the straight and neat furrows, but remark when one of them is less than perfect. 'My ol' dad, he'd say that look like a dog's piddle in the snow ...' they declare, and burst into a laugh so deep that you know it is coming from the heart. Then you plough a near perfect furrow, but they won't say anything about that one.

Our next hymn was *It Came Upon a Midnight Clear*. My ranging mind swung towards Alice, our sow, who is due her second litter on New Year's Eve. I know she will have them at midnight because it was at that time she started when her first litter was born. Except that was in June, when a midnight dash to check the sty was quite pleasant. If things are going to get deep and crisp and even, Alice may have to improvise. I have already intimated that there is ample precedent for mothers having to manage when there is no crib for a bed and I think Alice has got the message – I caught her shunting straw into corners yesterday.

'The cattle are lowing ...' sang the choir. Of course they are. The bull arrived last week and his presence has put my maiden heifers completely off their food. Where once they used to issue a coarse, rasping 'mooo' towards feeding time, they now moan a seductive melody which leads me to believe there will be little trouble from them this Christmas.

Heartened by that thought, the Christmas spirit briefly wafted over me. Even when the soloist rose to sing the *Boar's Head Carol* I didn't allow the thought of a freezerful of unsold pork joints to disturb me. Then we sang 'While shepherds watched ...' and I remembered the battery on the electric fence. It is flat and the flock will be roaming. God rest ye merry gentlemen? Some hope.

A Christmas present that is not worth discussing by the time the Twelve Days are over was probably not worth receiving in the first place; so I make no apology for a delayed account of one of the most precious gifts I have ever received.

I thought my extensive wardrobe of farming clothes was complete, but Santa had other ideas. On Christmas eve, we went across to Dilly's to wish the old boy a Merry Christmas. We sang a verse of a carol, hammered on the door and loaded him with mince pies and a bottle of rum, and were just about to leave when he called, 'Hang on, I've got something for yer.' He went upstairs and returned laden with the most massive duffel-coat I have seen. It was clearly of some age and might well have been worn by Jack Hawkins in *The Cruel Sea*, were it not that as I got closer to it the tang was less of salt than of stale milking-parlour. No matter, it was in fine condition and probably made of far better cloth than a similar garment today. There is a moth-hole or two but none sufficiently large to admit a gale of wind; and from the moment I slipped my arms into the fusty-smelling cloth I knew that this was it. At last my trouser basket would have a jewel in its crown. Lambing is about to start and as I leave the warmth of the house for the farm-yard I shall don it with the solemnity with which a monarch would receive his coronation robes, for this garment is worthy of no less respect. Thank you Dilly, thank you.

A farm is a very useful thing to have at Christmas. In fact, my observant brother-in-law has often remarked at great family gatherings that if I did not have a farm to escape to I would have to invent one. The truth is that by mid-afternoon on Christmas Day when the dusk is beginning to fall, the family have eaten enough fodder to fatten a prize bull and the house is deep enough in wrapping paper to provide a decent bed for a flock of sheep, nothing is more welcome than half an hour's excuse to feed the livestock. On a large farm it is no doubt a chore; but if you are organised you can whip round ours in thirty minutes and then return refreshed to eat and drink some more. It is one of the few days in the year when the pigs' eating habits are eclipsed by our own.

This year we had a crisp, clear and frosty Christmas Day and my regular afternoon round would have been a pleasure were it not for the Large Black shadow that has been hanging over us this Christmas. Last weekend, while the crowds were gathering for our nativity play, the Three Kings were slipping on their dressing gowns and children tying tea-cloths round their heads, our Large Black sow, Phoebe, was dying. Of course, the show went on and I dashed from improvised stage to sty, to attend the vet and help him get her to her wobbly feet. In retrospect, I should have suspected something the night before when the feed-bowl was not quite empty. Phoebe was probably the greediest pig we have ever raised, and her obsession with food was such that she would assume the slightest sound to be a harbinger of fodder. Certainly, it was not possible to open the back door of the house without her beginning to squeal, even if she had only been fed twenty minutes previously.

Having known her as a robust animal all her life, it was sad to see the life ebb from her; and it was equally confusing for her litter of piglets, who could not understand why the ever-providing mother had suddenly run dry. The vet came twice and did his best but it was clear that she was not going to live. I knew an old horseman who swore he could take one look at a sick horse and know its chances of survival. 'Yer can smell death on a horse,' he said, but I hardly believed him then. I do now. Farmers get to know their stock so well that they can read them like a book. Perhaps, had I not been so preoccupied with the nativity play, I might have read between the lines and spotted earlier that the pig was not well.

We gave her a grim little burial, the knacker-man not being interested in pig-meat. Robert and I took our spades and dug a grave in what was thankfully easily-dug, sandy soil. In none of the books I have read is there ever any praise for the skills of the grave-digger, but digging a decent hole is no mean task. I went to a country funeral a few weeks ago and, never being able to resist the temptation to kick the soil with the toe of my foot to see 'what sort o' land that be' I glanced down the perfectly shaped hole dug out of the most vicious, sticky and weighty clay. Digging that hole was no five minute job for a boy.

But our grave-digging had its lighter moments. 'Shall we drop her in Viking-style,' suggested Robert, but I did not want to think of old

Phoebe standing to attention six feet under. Instead, we dug a little deeper than we planned; we did not want to fill the hole and find we had trotters still waving in the air. And with the somewhat cheering thought from Robert that not many farm animals are lucky enough to die in their sleep, our grim little procession began. The cold rain, carried on a northerly wind, poured on us as we hauled the dead pig onto our sledge and hauled her up the farm. Her litter of seven did not even give her a glance as we pulled her out of the sty past them, neither did Alice, her mother, give her even a nod of recognition as we lumbered past. Phoebe was a good old pig, a fine mother to five litters, and we shall miss her.

It is said, superstitiously, that to ensure good fortune for the coming year, the last to leave the household in the old year must be black, and first thing over the threshold at the beginning of the new must be black as well. We have had our black departure and, as you read this, will be looking hard for the black sign that tells us there is a more fortunate year ahead.

I do not know any shepherds who watch their flocks by night these days, do you? I guess that in the days when Cyrenius was governor of Syria, and fencing was not very much in fashion, it did make sense to sit out on a hillside all night making sure the sheep did not wander. But these days, what with electric fencing, there is little point abiding in the fields watching a little red light pulse in rhythm with the 2,000 volt kick that modern units give. I would warn anyone who is not familiar with these things that contact with the live wire whilst seated on the ground does surely cause a brief electrical glory to shine all around.

But this Christmas Eve, I may well be doing a little abiding with the flock myself after a miraculous incident of a few days ago. With Robert, the occasional farm-hand, and Flash, the sheep dog, I took a stroll to the meadow at the top of the farm where the sheep are spending the first part of the winter. We have decided to have our lambing a little later this year and so, rather than spend dark January nights stumbling round the lambing yard, we have put it off till the longer days of late February. Normally I like to get lambing started as soon as possible after the New Year, since it not only provides a cast-iron excuse to get out of the house for brief spells coinciding with the Christmas visits of distant relations – 'how nice to see you ... thought I saw a wobbly ewe up the hill ... won't be more than a couple of hours ... oh what a shame ... well, see you next year then' – but it gets a bit of frosty air in the lungs and a sweat on the brow after too much indulgence and confinement. But last January was so wet and miserable and early March so mild and lush that I am betting on the same happening again this year, fool that I am. Anyway, it is too late to change my mind. Back in October, the rams were put to the flock with a view to lambing starting the last week in February.

Imagine then our surprise as we strolled up the farm, to see a tiny white smudge on the distant horizon. We stood and gazed and swore it looked for all the world like a new-born lamb. I said to Robert it could not possibly be, and he agreed. It was nonsense to think we could have a lamb this early. It is roughly five months from conception to birth and a lamb now would be nothing short of a miracle. 'Fear not,' said he, it will be an old feed bag, or a few seagulls huddling together.

More than a little dread was filling my troubled mind and as we drew closer to the suspect white package, it was clear that there were to be no glad tidings of great joy. It was indeed a newly-born lamb. But how? Begotten, not created? Or was it possible that one of those precocious young ram lambs from last season who we forgot to castrate and to which we did not give a second thought...? But surely not, they looked so small and incapable.

Now, my attitude to this miracle may seem rather churlish, but you have to see it from my point of view: how many more of these woolly swines are playing the innocent virgin and about to deliver surprise Christmas blessings? The mild weather has made the grass unseasonably lush and the ewes are all so fat that if I were to judge their pregnant state from their size, I would mark them all down as about to deliver a donkey.

Anyway, I have my heart set on a peaceful holiday; but what sort of break is it going to be with obstetrical emergencies at all hours of the day? And how will the family react if I am forced to carve the turkey still wearing my veterinary rubber glove? Even worse, we have nowhere to house the ewes for winter lambing. We usually bring them all to the yard; but it needs clearing, and strawing, and as time is pressing there is no certainty the job could be done. I shall have to tell them there is no room in the inn; and anyway they did away with the manger last winter, breaking it in several places by butting it with their thick heads. We haven't got round to fixing it yet.

It would be a mistake to offer you a review of the year on this farm. It has been far from vintage and, looking back, days of despair have sprouted like weeds amongst a thin crop of successes. But we are still here; and since I have learnt that in farming only the present moment matters and the events of days gone by are as much use as an empty sack of feed, I am putting a cheery face on things and looking forward with optimism, I hope we shall have rather more luck in the coming twelve months. So let us have a celebration.

No one else is going to give us an award, no sword is ever likely to tap this farmer's shoulder in be recognition of his contribution to agriculture, no gong ever be pinned to the chest – not even one "for tenacity against all the odds". So I have decided that I shall create my own awards, like the self-congratulatory ones that film and television people seem to enjoy so much. The trouble is, it is difficult to dream up the categories.

I suppose if I were to give an award for the Best Situation Comedy of the Year, it would have to be given to Robert, the farm-hand, and a big black boar pig who has no name that could be printed. The situation occurred when this boar pig, and the rest of the litter, had to be loaded into a trailer to be moved. As is so often the case with a litter of pigs, there is always one which either does not get the idea of what is going on, and panics; or – and this is the worst to deal with – knows precisely what is going on and does not wish to join in. The other pigs readily answered the feed bucket and with a little coaxing and persuasion, trotted up the ramp and happily munched away, not caring that they were captured. He did not give in so easily. Instead, he fled. When Robert tried to corner him, the pig's body, slippery with an unspeakable mixture of muck and mud, slid easily through his hands. We tried persuasion again but the pig was now filled with the spirit of the chase. I suggested we left him and let him get even fatter; Robert, who enjoys a rugby tackle, offered to have one more go.

Creeping stealthily towards the resting animal, Robert grabbed both his back legs and held on for grim death. The pig was not going to give in. Alas, Robert slipped, and the scene which wins him the comedy category was of Robert being dragged, face down through the mire, arms outstretched, creating a bow-wave of pig muck with his chin as he slid. A worthy winner, Mr Bean could not have been funnier.

But that's about it, really, as far as highlights go. The only other category might be for the Least Promising Newcomer. I would unreservedly award that to the young cart-horse Prince who had many talents, but farm work was not one of them. Do not get me wrong, he was a fine-looking horse, a strong puller, a kindly horse, too. But farm work demands a special temperament both in horses and people. It requires a complete submission to the task in hand: no questioning or doubting the way a task has to be performed, just getting on with it. We have had young lads work here who have tried to persuade me of better ways of accomplishing tasks, wanting to try their supposedly labour-saving methods and fly in the face of generations of experience; usually I let them try in their way and discover, to their discomfort, why mine was better. With a horse you can't afford to let it try its own way. There is no room for a cart-horse to start having ideas of his own, as young Prince had, and so he has gone to a home more suited to his particular talents.

But I cannot end the year on such a low note, typical though it would be of a farmer. So I must give my final award, a sort of Lifetime Achievement Award, to dear Alice the Large Black Sow. Not that she has done much this year, except wallow a lot, and feed (that never seems to stop showbiz people getting lifetime awards, though, does it?). She hasn't even managed a litter of piglets despite a lengthy romance with Murphy the boar, so I suspect she has put all that sort of thing behind her. But she is as regal as ever, making the occasional public appearance when visitors come to the farm, just to let her subjects know that she still reigns, happy and glorious, over this little farm.

I seem to remember there is an old superstition: in order to guarantee luck for the coming year, the first thing to cross the threshold on the first day of the new year, must be black. As Alice deserves the honour, and we need the luck, I am contemplating offering her an invitation. As long as she does not insist on being kissed under the mistletoe, or joining trotters for *Auld Lang Syne*, it might just bring the luck we need.

FOURTEEN

As we approached the end of the decade which had started with my first, faltering ploughing lessons, and ended with the entire farmyard crammed with animals and children enjoying our third nativity play, it was becoming clear that the adventure was coming to an end. It is worth remembering that it was an adventure, an expedition into an unknown world, a journey of discovery. It was never a 'lifestyle' choice. I did not take myself to the farming life because I expected it to be some kind of heaven on earth, I knew too much about the reality of it for that, In fact, it was the sheer, blatant, blunt reality of it that drove me on. It was not a *Good Life*, but it was Real Life. And the sharpest contrast from my other worlds of radio and television.

I am often asked why I stopped doing it? But examine the question, and then ask yourself if you would enquire the same of a man who had just scaled Everest? The achievement has been made, the total experience has been had, there is nothing to be gained from prolonging it and repeating it. And besides, the body becomes weary. As I type this now, my wrists flash with pain, the scars of farming wear and tear. And there was another reason I decided to stop – I was becoming a real farmer and I did not like what I saw.

I got to the point where I suddenly noticed that an entire farming year has passed without any mention of the corn harvest; no invective spat in the direction of the infuriating binder, no cursing at the virile weeds which humble any attempt I make at growing wheat, oats or barley.

Well, the truth is that there has not been a corn harvest this year because I did not plant any. This is causing some rejoicing in the household, for an entire August has passed without fierce displays of harvest-related mood and temper. To be honest, I have quite enjoyed it too; and so I have declared a complete cessation of corn-growing on this farm. The question my long-suffering family are asking is whether I intend to make this a "permanent" rather than merely a "complete" cessation. I am not giving any more away and will continue to play my cards close to my chest. I may decide to sell the thrashing machine as a sort of laying-down of arms, but I have the use of another one up my sleeve so my actions cannot be taken at face value.

However, I have decided things are going have to change on this little farm. I can only sum up my new attitude as being one of back-to-basics. I have been farming, organically, with horses, for nearly five years now and only recently have I come to realise how far I have become removed from my original aims and ambitions.

Somehow, I have been sucked into a mainstream farming way of thinking: I have started to be obsessed with yields, calving intervals, nutritional data and all the other hideous jargon which modern farmers have erected to distance the layman from any understanding of what they do. Slowly and insidiously I have been deflected from my ambition of farming in a way in which I believed, into some kind of futile attempt to keep up with those around me. Which, with only a pair of cart-horses and my two hands, was bound to end in tears. I warn all those who might follow in my path to keep their eyes and hearts fixed firmly on their original intentions and never let them stray.

The turning point came for me when I picked up a book I first read when I started to keep pigs, and have not read since. It is called *The*

Pioneering Pig by Norman Blake and was published in the early fifties by Faber and Faber along with a whole raft of highly sensible books on alternative approaches to farming.

Blake's approach is boldly stated in his second paragraph; "I am writing this book because I love pigs. They are wise and they are active; they don't wait for something to turn up – they turn it up themselves." He says that the best way of deciding what a pig needs "is to find out what the pig wants and supply it." He does not hesitate to advise that pigs are just as happy to live under and old wagon or elevator as in some constructed shed. All this I read, and devoured, and decided made sense, when Alice, the Large black sow, first arrived on the farm, I saw that Norman Blake had written the nearest thing to a perfect small-scale pig-keepers creed as I could possibly imagine.

But somehow my faith got diluted by long discussions with butchers about "back fat probes" and arguments with dreary professional pig-keepers about "growth rates." I almost dared to hijack an old wagon and build a pig hut out of it, but some farmer came a long and told me concrete would be better, and for some reason I believed him. I thought at one stage I might fatten pigs on tares, a green leafy plant full of protein and goodness. But I got laughed at for that and was told that the feed merchant had some nice "cubes", and although I never bought any I guiltily assumed they would be better.

But re-reading Norman Blake I now realise that I have quite a way to travel in reverse gear before I get back to my starting point. I once built a pig-sty out of ash-poles and bales of straw and it was perfectly adequate and lasted a whole season, but since then I have bought miserable corrugated-tin arcs, because somehow I had got the message they were better. Blake would never have been so foolish.

How, then, do you break the news to a pig that it is time to move on? What words do you say to a faithful old servant which can fully convey the turmoil which is about to engulf her life and all our lives, for that matter, now we have decided to sell the farm.

Somehow or other Alice, the Large Black sow, will have to be told. After all, she was the first piece of livestock on this farm and it is right that she should be the first to know the news. Before you shed a tear or stifle a cheer, let me explain that this could be the start of an extremely long goodbye. Too many words have already been written about the state of the property market for me to have to explain any further. Selling farms is an even slower business. Nevertheless, a dapper estate agent has been appointed, Mr Simpson, who has already presented us with a very likely future farmer of this land.

If all this comes as a surprise to you, it is a shock to me too. I embarked upon this experiment knowing that it would be of finite duration; but ten years after my first footsteps down the furrow, I still had no inkling it was time for it to come to an end, until the middle of the summer when the thought first struck me.

The prospect of another farming year was looming, with all that this implied. Six more cold and wet months trudging through the cattle yard, then spring cultivations; hardly a break before lambing then it would be sowing mangel-wurzels and hoeing them, a quick breath before haymaking, and another year would be gone. But not till the binder and thrashing machine had been faced up to. Having ridden that roundabout for six years, farming in a classical style with my own two hands and virtually full-time, I want to get off.

Some will be laughing up their sleeves, '... oh, he couldn't take it. Too 'ard for him, it was.' Well, I prefer to think of it as having studied hard for a degree and having passed. If not with flying colours then with a modest amount of distinction. I took on this land, improved it in my estimation, fenced and watered it, brought old barns back from a crumbling brink. I have learned horseman's skills, some of which are almost lost, given my neighbours a few laughs. I am not yet exhausted, but can well see that within five years I might be. This is not a complete break, you understand; our beloved cart-horses come wherever we go, which limits our choice of future address. I guess it rules out Canary Wharf.

What is life like without a farm? I can hardly remember. Nor can I envisage a life where the weather or the seasons are not in charge of every minute of the day. I had forgotten that there are people who do jobs where it does not matter if it is an icy February day or a balmy April afternoon, but I doubt I can learn to live that sort of life

185

again. Eventually, I shall come round to making an assessment of what has been achieved and learnt here. But for the moment I am a bit numbed. We all are.

The one thing I am going to miss is being able to step instantly and effortlessly onto what might be called the "moral high ground." To give you an example; when I have been late for a meeting through disorganisation or lack of interest, I have been able to apologise and mutter 'calf in the ditch, terribly lucky to get it out. Sorry to be late.' It never fails to work. All sympathy is focused on the calf, I am the hero and everyone forgets the time. If all the people to whom I have given that apology were to get together, they would conclude that this farm spends most of its time giving swimming lessons to livestock. If it's you, I am sorry.

But there are more private pleasures too. Last week I had to meet media moguls in that corporate TV headquarters on the South Bank. As I crossed the threshold which has regularly seen everyone from Bruce Forsyth to Ant and Dec, it gave me some personal pleasure to look up at all twenty storeys and think to myself that I was probably the only person here today who had buried a dead sheep before breakfast. A silly, private pleasure. But I shall miss it.

Of course, some retiring farmers never come to terms with the loss of their land. I know of one who foolishly thought that when he owned land, he somehow had "a position in the community." He assumed this from the deferential way the Boy Scouts knocked on his door pleading to set up a camp, or the annual Church ramble humbly asked permission to trudge through his thickets. In truth, he had no position at all. Everyone had the measure of the man and turned his grandiose notions to their advantage. Call him "sir" for long enough when you meet him in the street, and it will be no time before he lends you a meadow for a football pitch. I have never been in that league. No one has ever turned up here, doffing their cap. I have no status to lose.

Instead, the only thing I have been able to offer the community is gossip. Naturally we were heavily gossiped about when we first came here; it was said that I was opening a themed adventure park complete with wild animals. In a way, I suppose that came true. The other bit of gossip which has developed a huge head of steam is that: 'They've 'ad the bailiffs in.' This, I have to admit, is based on some evidence. It is true that a man in a suit was seen to arrive on the farm, ask for the keys of our aged Land-Rover and drive off in it. Ahh, Watson! It could only be the bailiffs. Actually, it was Roy the mechanic, who does the MOT and service. He had come to collect it, suited, on his way to the in-laws for a smart night out. The Land Rover was returned two days later; but the professional gossips never seem to add that sort of evidence into their theories. Nor did they spot that such is the decrepit state of that vehicle that no respectable bailiff would be seen dead with it. It is worthless. It would be like the receivers going into Barings and seizing the ball points.

I suppose there will be more rumours, so let me just issue a few denials before they gather too much ground. For a start, I am not and never have been Lord Lucan. Working a traditional farm with cart-horses and usually covered in muck would, I admit, be a jolly good cover and I bet Lucan, if alive, has often wished he thought of it. Nor is it true that our senior cart-horse, Star, is in fact Shergar who has put on a bit of weight. I must also deny that I gambled away all the winter fodder on the derivatives market in Singapore, that I am the fifth Beatle or the sixth man. Is all that clear?

Yes, pride and prejudice; I have them both in abundance. Now that the end of my farming career is looming, my large and troublesome brood must be disposed of. The sheep, pigs, cattle and, yes, even the machinery must be found good homes. They must marry well and not just for love, but for a decent bit of money too. Mrs Bennett has all my sympathy.

Like her, I see most of my daughters as deserving. I am perhaps a bit more careful than her, though: the livestock are certainly not going to market where bounders like Mr Wickham can go bidding for them and carry them off to an unsuitable fate. I shall inspect all their future homes before they leave the farm, and satisfy myself that they have made good matches. However (and I would not wish her to hear me say this) our old sow Alice is now very slow on her feet, stone deaf, and at the end of her piglet-bearing days. She may be destined to stay on the shelf. She is as much a worry to me as Mary probably ended up to Mrs Bennett. At least if I end up with her still at home, she doesn't play the piano and quote scripture all day.

Sage, the British White cow is Jane: as good as she is beautiful, willing to lick the boots of any man who pays her the slightest attention. She will have no trouble finding her Mr. Bingley. The silly and flirtatious sheep are a different matter; they would run after any troop of licentious soldiery, especially if it had a bucket of sugar-beet nuts, and may well end up in the clutches of some ill-bred ram. Serve them right.. But, I promise you, I shall deploy all available uncles with horsewhips to ensure that they are properly treated.

The next step is somehow to bolster my faith that it is a truth universally acknowledged that a single man in possession of a good fortune, must be in want of a threshing-machine. Is there a Darcy or a Bingley out there (preferably with a fortune) who might care for a threshing machine and binder? Here I become more desperate and callous like my role-model: frankly, Mr Collins can have either of them. The trouble with all this aged farming gear is that, unlike the radiant Sage, or Bilberry the Red Poll cow, the machinery's appeal is quite narrow. Actually, I cannot imagine anybody other than me who wants it. None of it is worthy of a space in a museum, yet neither is any of it so commonplace as to earn a home on the scrap-heap.

So may I describe the virtues of these two machines in the hope that love might blossom? I cannot speak for their utter fidelity: I do understand that falling in love with a bit of farming gear can be a heart-breaking business. But as Mr Bennett said "next to being married, a girl likes to be crossed in love a little now and then", and why should not the same be true of men?

And it does have a certain bloom. My Ransomes Thrashing Machine is gloriously pink, freshly painted a couple of years ago a delicate shade not unlike a blushing maiden's cheeks. I did love her then, truly I did. She is of magnificent stature, a noble lass who hums and she works to take the long straws of cut corn and turn them into straw and grain. A giving girl. At least she was, until her breakdown. That was a day to remember. She started all sweetness and light, happily going about her daily tasks, sighing a little as was her way but always willing. Till there was a bang. Her innards collapsed. It was not just a physical breakdown, her spirit was crushed too. She suffered endless hours under the surgeon's spanner, but it was down to me to instil in her the will to thresh once again. At the moment she's fine, but she certainly needs a Mr Darcy.

You see my dilemma? It is beginning to get me down. It is enough to have to find one husband for each of my family, but almost impossible to find a bigamist who wants to wed two of my daughters. As Mrs Bennett said, "Nobody is on my side, nobody takes part with me: I am cruelly used, nobody feels for my poor nerves."

Before the farm finally closes down, I really must ring one of the Bond Street auction houses to ensure that my works of art are disposed of in an manner that befits their true worth. I can picture the scene: bidders will be sitting, hushed and tight-lipped, those wispy, well bred girls will be hanging on telephones listening for bids from the Amsterdam dealers, the auctioneer will take a sip of cooling water before braving himself to announce, 'Lot 52. A fine example, possibly the only one of its kind still to be used, reputedly swung by the master of the craft, farmworker Dilly Sharp, One Mangel-topping knife! About 1932. What am I offered? Twenty thousand guineas? Very well, a fiver anybody?'

You can laugh, but it is parting with my collection of little treasures that is more likely to bring a tear to the eye than closing the barn door for the last time. I can honestly say that I shall not feel much emotion at the thought of never having to hump lousy bales of straw again, but when I consider that I may have no further use for my bill-hook, finely honed sheep shears, or patent pig-catching device circa 1925, then I start to feel desperately sad.

To me, these farming hand tools are true works of art. They have been developed and fine-tuned over centuries till a point about fifty years ago when they had reached the peak of their perfection. Then came the great eclipse; the huge mechanical shadow spread across them and farmers threw their old friends aside to rust and rot. Since I have been farming I have been rescuing tools like these with the fervour of a Salvationist saving souls. I have rummaged through scrap heaps if my eye has caught the rusty remains of a hedge slasher; I have stood at farm auctions frozen to the marrow, waiting for the very last lot which might have been a ditching shovel or a particularly fine example of a grain scoop. I like to think I have been sensible about it. I have bought only things for which I thought I had a use. This policy has led to some anguished moments: I remember standing, torn, looking at a yoke as used by milkmaids to carry two pails of milk, one from each shoulder. Being prone to a stiff neck I doubted I would ever use it, nor did I expect it to get a particularly warm welcome from the farmer's wife, so I let it go. I still grieve.

It is time to ring down the curtain on the show. For much of the time it has been farce, occasionally tragicomedy; we have been laughed at when we were being deadly serious, taken seriously when all we wanted was to raise a smile. Perhaps pantomine sums it up better. 'Behind you !' Yes, it's all behind us now.

So we thought we would come on stage, take a final bow, and thank you for being a wonderful audience. Of course, in setting up a final family photograph, there were backstage tantrums. Sage, the British White cow, would only appear if she could be at the front of the picture but the photographer told her she was too brilliant to be in the foreground. Fortunately, she misunderstood his technical observation as flattery, and so graciously accepted a place on the second row. That was a close one.

Flash the sheepdog took some persuading too. You see, he's terrified of sheep. I am sorry if it embarrasses him but he would do anything to avoid confronting a ewe. If you don't believe me, look carefully and you will see he is on a lead. The sheep, having some care for his feelings, played the part of the chorus with decorum and kept more or less in the positions they were given. If they moved, they knew I would have to send Flash to sort them out and it would only end in tears. His tears.

The cart horses weren't easy either. I am holding Taffy and Blue. Blue came when we started to farm, has lived through all the hard bits, and so surely deserves top billing. Taffy, on the other hand, is a youngster still learning the game, but he and Blue are the principal working pair now. Which puts poor old Star on the back row, which he does not like. He was working before either of the ones up front were born, has pulled ploughs more miles than those two have had hot bran mashes. So why isn't he up front, like the veterans on D Day, being saluted and honoured? Where's the justice? I suppose because he is the most trustworthy. I didn't have to keep looking round for mischief. Only the red cow, Bilberry, is without temperament. We have had good cows and bad cows, but she has been the best. We have had cows that charge through hedges like an army on manoeuvres: skittish, girly ones who thought it would be super fun to flatten a fence. Bilberry has never put a foot wrong. She is quite happy just to play a part, grateful to come on stage for the grand finale. Contentedly pregnant with her latest calf, she is the sort of cow who would share a dressing room with anyone, and make the rest of the cast a cup of tea after the show is over.

Which brings us to the supporting cast, the humans. In our long-running panto Dilly has been without doubt the conjurer. He has more tricks up his sleeve than a meeting of the Magic Circle. He has been the master of the mangel-topping knife, has amazed you with the deftness with which he has wielded his hoe. The swiftness of the hand deceives the eye. But do not let him start on his comedy routine. He has only one joke, which starts 'We only ever used to grow four mangels…' and when you look at him, puzzled, he goes on, '… one in each corner of the field and we rolled 'em home!' Yes, you've heard it before, and so have we. He can stick to magic.

Then comes young Robert White. What a star he has been, performing like a cross between an acrobat and a commando as he showed us his piglet-catching routine. Torvill and Dean could learn a thing or two about balance by watching this lad move in pursuit of an uncooperative hog. Blending the determination of the SAS with the ruggedness of a rugby prop forward, he always got his pig.

Then there is Derek, the horseman who gave up the land nearly forty years ago when the farm on which he worked replaced the cart-horses with tractors. With us, he has managed to fill a gap in his life. He too is a bit of a magician. I remember the day he drove the seed drill across the field for the first time in over thirty years. He had not spoken a word of command to a horse in all that time, but they obeyed, walked straight, and the sprouting corn eventually showed that the lines in which the drill have been driven were as precise as if drawn with a pencil on a map. In our show he is the mind-reader; the thoughts of the horses are no secret to him. You would rise to your feet to applaud if you could see Derek and the horses, telepathically in action.

Then comes Richard White, Farmer White as he has been billed. He has been our stage manager and propped us up when the scenery looked set to fall upon us, or our inexperienced feet blunder down some unsuspected trapdoor. He marked our entrances and exits and when things went wrong he helped with the improvisation. Another star, in his way.

But now the show is over. 'Oh No It Isn't' some of you have cried out, but oh, yes it is; for sure. It has been exhilarating, invigorating, inspiring, depressing, crushing, wearing, thrilling and overwhelming, sometimes all at once. It is time to take a long, exhausted breath.

And what will become of the cast? I am pleased to announce that they have all found good homes in which their individual shows can go on. As I have said before, the cart-horses stay with us wherever we go. Bilberry, the red cow, is going to a farm down the lane which has not had Red Poll cows since an award-winning herd was dispersed in the 1940's. She has pioneering work to do, founding a new dynasty.

As for the sheep, for no reason I can think of Farmer White wants them. To my shame I have taken money off him for them. I should be paying him to take them away. To ease my conscience I have thrown in the elderly sheep dog as part of the package. Working dogs need to be kept working and, although in Flash's case it is difficult to be certain whether he would be happier with his sheep than without them, on balance I decided he must stay at his post, with the flock. He will probably hate me for it, but I am reliably informed by those who care for the aged that a challenge – however unwelcome – staves off senility better than anything.

Sage has done best for herself. She has been sold to neighbours, a young chap and his wife well used to keeping livestock. You'll never guess what he does for a living: he recycles waste from chocolate factories into animal feed! True. Sage has found this out and her bags have been packed for weeks. This cow imagines herself sitting under the shade of a tree, decadently scoffing a misshapen *Turkish Delight*, or incestuously licking a reject bar of *Dairy Milk*.

Which leaves me, the only one with an undecided future. The potential buyer who turned up in August full of ideas and enthusiasm for a life on the land has quietly faded away. I cannot say I blame him. Forgive me for being less than modest for a moment, but having a farm of your own, getting your hands dirty and your back bent, calls for a fair amount of courage and determination. If you are lacking in either you had better not start. It was as well he realised before it was too late.

But if your mind is set on the land, I would not try and talk you out of it. You'll have to take all the jokes about the "good life"; the sneers of some farmers who will resent the pleasure they see you getting from it. Aching and nervous, broke and sleepless, you will have to put up with the weekend visitors cooing sentimentally at your "idyllic" life.

But you will emerge from it a broader individual, having come as close to the forces of nature as it is possible to be these days in Britain. Nor does it do anyone any harm to have to face up to the cruel facts of farming life: the death of much loved animals, the reassurance that comes from the birth of new ones. Oh yes, I am a wiser individual for my time on the land. My family probably learned a thing or two as well, but I have not dared to ask them exactly what.